C000060533

WHEN
STARS
WHISPER

WHEN
STARS
WHISPER

A Midwinter Mystery

Heather Elvidge

HareSay
BOOKS

© Heather Elvidge, 2021

Published by HareSay Books

All rights reserved. No part of this book may be reproduced, adapted, stored in a retrieval system or transmitted by any means, electronic, mechanical, photocopying, or otherwise without the prior written permission of the author.

The rights of Heather Elvidge to be identified as the author of this work have been asserted in accordance with the Copyright, Designs and Patents Act 1988.

A CIP catalogue record for this book is available from the British Library.

ISBN 978-1-7399818-0-8

Book layout and design by Clare Brayshaw

Prepared and printed by:

York Publishing Services Ltd
64 Hallfield Road
Layerthorpe
York YO31 7ZQ

Tel: 01904 431213

Website: www.yps-publishing.co.uk

Contents

1

The Steadfast Star

Ross was drifting away when he heard the girl. He wanted to sleep but she would not let him. She slapped his face. She shook him by the shoulders. Her words were meaningless, an urgent confusion of sounds. Ross turned away to curl up in the snow. Sleep was so close, so tempting. "Go away," he mumbled. "Leave me alone."

The girl took no notice. Strong hands gripped his arms, and dragged him to his feet. She peered at him out of a halo of fur, then face and fur disappeared, and his right arm was pulled across her shoulders. Ross felt her other arm across his back. He tried a step, nearly dragging them both down. She said nothing, just shifted her hold to take more of his weight.

Ross was so cold he could only shuffle, making their progress painfully slow. After a while he gave up trying, and let her haul him through the snow. In his chilled and sleepy state he hardly noticed the shape forming out of the darkness until, roused by barking, he heard a woman's voice. He saw light, warm and inviting. Half-lifted, half-pushed, Ross stumbled into a room where he slumped, exhausted, to the floor.

In front of him burned a fire ringed with stones, where logs glowed red-gold. Trails of smoke were drifting upwards past a big, black pot suspended from a pole. A musky, smoky smell wafted on the air, unfamiliar but not unpleasant.

A dog came to sniff at him. It was huge, hairy, and stared suspiciously. His rescuers shooed it away, then knelt down on either side. Each took a frozen hand, kneading it gently until the warmth began to return. Ross looked quickly from one to the other.

"Who're you?"

The girl said something he didn't catch. She let go of his hand to throw off her big coat, revealing a short, collarless jacket with coloured bands down the front. Her dark hair was caught in a scruffy plait, and a long suede skirt spread around her on the floor. The clothes looked strange, but no stranger than everything else.

"What's happening? Where is this?" Ross asked, pulling his other hand from the woman's grip. Her stare was a bit friendlier than the dog's, yet not by much. With her round, creased face, and grey hair creeping from a deerskin cap, she resembled a granny from an old folktale. Around her shoulders was a shawl patterned with flowers – otherwise her clothes were similar to the girl's.

"Tilda," the girl said, tapping her shoulder. "Tilda." Then she placed a hand on the woman's arm. "Hirta." Exhaustion was stealing Ross away, yet he managed a weak smile. The girl smiled back, holding out her hands as if to catch his words.

"I'm Ross," he said.

"Eimross," she repeated.

Suddenly the woman rose up, shaking dust and dog hairs from her skirt. She leaned over the fire to the cooking pot, and gave the contents a quick stir. While she ladled something into a small wooden bowl, Ross tried to wake up. He did feel hungry. It seemed like years since his last meal of sausage and chips.

Hirta passed him the bowl, along with a wooden spoon. Then she stood with hands on hips, nodding encouragement. From the other side of the hearth four brown eyes followed every move. The black dog had a younger companion who seemed keen to help the stranger out, should he suddenly lose his appetite.

Cradling the warm bowl in his hands, Ross looked down into the steaming depths. It was a kind of stew, of no particular colour, with a slight film of grease floating on the top. As he watched, small chunks of meat bobbed to the surface, followed by a lump of yellowish fat.

Eurgh. He couldn't eat that. But the girl and the woman seemed kind, so he didn't want to upset them. Also, he was starving, and there didn't seem to be anything else. Ross eyed the stew again. At least the meat looked lean. He took a cautious sip – the flavour, although strong, was not at all bad. Soon all that was left in the bowl was the yellow blob.

While he was eating Hirta was making up a bed. It looked snug and welcoming, like a huge nest, so when she beckoned him over Ross did not hesitate. The girl was pointing to a wooden bucket. Then she bobbed up and down, pretending to sit on it. Ross scowled. Something else he didn't understand. Maybe this was one of those living history experiments, where people dress up to live like they did in the past. He climbed onto the bed, wondering if it was safe with all that creaking, before deciding he didn't care, and sinking back gratefully.

It was then Ross realised the purpose of the bucket. He hoped with all his heart that he would not need to use it.

~

Tilda and her grandmother draped another reindeer hide over their visitor, and settled down beside the fire to talk. The older dog squeezed in between them, yawning and stretching.

"Well, this is a strange thing," Hirta said, poking at the logs to make them blaze up. "Anyone would think he came down with the snow."

"Lying there all alone, he was," Tilda replied. "He could have frozen."

"He would have, but for you." Hirta placed another log on the fire. "Those clothes! Useless." They sat in silence for a while, watching the flames flickering in the hearth. The only other movement was from the girl's hand as she stroked the dog's ears. Eventually Hirta said, "There is mystery here. We must be careful."

"Nanna, he is just a lad."

"All the same. Strangers never come out here in the long night. No proper clothes, no sled – where are his kinfolk? Someone is meddling with spirits, I can feel it." Tilda was surprised, although Nanna was never wrong about these matters. "You see," Hirta said quietly, "when I slept, I saw the white fox watching us."

Tilda knew from Nanna's manner that this was a true dream. You could always tell, because they were so clear. Sometimes the Old Ones came with insight, or foresight. Sometimes it was an animal, like the white fox.

"Something means us harm," Tilda whispered, touching the reindeer amulet that hung at her neck. Hirta clutched her bear's tooth – it had never failed to protect her. "Fetch the guardian," she said.

Tilda lifted down the rough, wooden figure that hung from one of the tent poles. It had been given to Nanna when she got her first tent, and before that had protected generations of their kinfolk. She laid the precious carving, dusty from the smoke, on a piece of reindeer hide. Then she took a bundle of dried herbs from a bag, and lit it from the fire. The tightly bound stems began to smoulder, releasing cleansing scents of juniper and sweet grasses.

Hirta scooped some fat from a birch box, and smeared it all over the guardian. She rubbed it lovingly into every cranny and crevice, deep into the wood. While she worked she whispered some verses, calling on the spirits of their forebears to protect them. When the charm was done, and the wood was well polished, the guardian was returned to its place on the tent pole.

"All is well," Tilda said, as she hung up the totem by its leather strap. Glancing over at the sleeping stranger, she thought how harmless he seemed. Surely the threat did not come from him. But whatever might happen the guardian would do its work, shielding them from harm.

"Ready for a bowl of tea?" Hirta asked. She was happier now, confident that the charm was working. So while Tilda poured tea from the battered metal pot, Hirta went over to check on their visitor. She found him sleeping soundly under the deer hides, with warm chest and hands. There was no sign of the chilled sleep that leads to the soul's passing. "Old Ma Frost has not breathed on him," she said. "The lad will live." She returned to sit beside the fire, and together they sipped tea while planning the next day's tasks.

"Those lines will need checking," Hirta said.

"I know. Should I take Eimross? He could help."

Hirta laughed. "You may as well take damp kindling. Work is a stranger to him – his hands are soft as a newborn's. As for his clothes–"

"We have spare leggings," Tilda suggested. "And my old boots."

Hirta frowned. "Mittens. I suppose he could have mine. We will see."

They finished their tea, and tidied the things from around the hearth. Hirta tended the fire so it would stay alive for a while, murmuring the old prayer to the hearth spirit. "Hearth-keeper bide with us, keep the flame as we lie dreaming. Warm the hearth, and soft the light, safe the souls that sleep tonight." Then she retired to her bed of branches and reindeer hides. "Not too long, Tilda."

Tilda was not ready for sleep. She knelt by the black dog that lay by the fire, head on paws, and looked over at the sleeping stranger. "Where is his home, Larna?" There was nothing of the forest about him, no trace of birch, or pine, or spruce. No smell of reindeer either, even though everything here smelt of deer. Larna was watching the stranger too, through barely-open eyes. Her nose twitched at scents she could not identify.

Tilda remembered how she had pushed Larna away. "Sorry, lass," she whispered. "You were only protecting us." The dog lifted her head to lick the girl's chin. Tilda hugged her, and smoothed the thick, black coat. She knew Larna would keep watch while they slept, just in case. Nanna was asleep, the covers pulled up to her chin. Already the air was vibrating with her snoring.

~

Ross was not sleeping. He had been awake all the time, even when the woman put her hand on his chest. He had wanted to sleep, but it was no use. It wasn't the low voices, or the smell of burning leaves, that kept him awake. It wasn't the chanting, or even the snoring. It was the thoughts chasing around in his head.

Lying in the snow feeling frozen, that was real. It was the things that couldn't be real that troubled him. The memories were so vivid. He lay still, trying to make sense of them.

It all began with the reindeer on the roof. There it stood, in the shadow of the chimneystack, pale as a winter moon. It was the most amazing thing he had ever seen.

Ross remembered looking sideways through the sloping loft window, cheek pressed hard against cold glass. But that was too awkward. He needed to open the window. He pushed at the bar, and the frame swung out. Icy air rushed in. A white velvety nose appeared briefly in the opening, followed by a deep blue eye that stared straight at him. A voice seemed to come from far away, yet at the same time it was inside his head. "Smell the air! Snow is coming," it said.

Ross was certain the voice belonged to the reindeer. It was not his own voice – the one he heard when he was thinking.

"Hurry," the reindeer said. "We have far to go."

What did it mean, we? Ross pushed the window out as far as it would go. "You can come in, if you like." The reindeer did not reply, simply tilted its head so its antlers came into full view. It was obvious they would not fit through the window.

What to do? It couldn't come in, and he couldn't go out. Sometimes Ross had been tempted, on those nights when he crept out of bed to see the stars instead of going to sleep. It was a stupid idea, and anyway it was forbidden. But it's not every night you find a reindeer on your roof. Ross wanted a proper look. Then somehow he was out in the freezing air, standing on the tiles beside the reindeer.

Now he was outside the creature looked smaller. Smaller and even stranger, if that were possible. Its body seemed too big for its pale, skinny legs. The antlers seemed too big for its head. And yet it was glorious. Its white hair shimmered in the starlight with hints of a thousand colours. Ross wanted to touch the soft-looking coat, but somehow that didn't seem right.

"You can talk," he said.

The reindeer gave him a hard look. "And you can hear."

"So how did you get on the roof?"

This was a silly question, and both of them knew it. The reindeer grunted. "See that, up there?" it said, lifting its nose to the sky. Ross gazed at the star, lonely in its patch of empty sky. This was something he knew all about. "That's Polaris, the pole star."

"Is it?" the reindeer said. "To us it is Steadfast, the star that guides us home. North, to the snow."

Ross pictured the north, the snowy lands where auroras happen. He had always wanted to see the Northern Lights. And now he did – their glowing colours were swirling inside his head, making him feel incredibly giddy.

The reindeer was watching him closely. "Go now, and we shall see them," it said. "Quick, onto the sled."

Perhaps Ross should have wondered how a sled had suddenly appeared, but because his head was spinning he was just grateful to sit down. Immediately, the reindeer started towards the edge of the roof. The sled lurched forward, jolting Ross into reality. Tumbling into the darkness, his room with the safe bed, and toast with berry jam, all jumbled into his head at once. "No!" he shouted.

The reindeer stopped, its front hooves bridging the gutter. Its antlers shook impatiently, sending a shiver rippling down its back. It asked what was the matter.

"What if I fall off?" Ross said. "I can't fly like you."

December's stars glittered in the blue-black sky. A meteor blazed a fiery trail, and vanished. On the roof, the reindeer fixed Ross with an intense stare. In the depths of its blue eyes golden sparks began to glow, as if the flaming meteor had fallen there. It was impossible to look away. There was only that voice, stronger than before, saying, "Trust in your fate. We will soar among the stars. The wonders you will see will burn in you forever."

The voice poured midnight into Ross's mind, smoothing away fear until he felt as weightless as starshine. He heard himself say, "Ready. Let's go." At once the reindeer sprang into the air, dragging the sled after it. They floated over the apple tree, and up towards the stars. Ross saw his house drop away, folded into the darkness.

All around in the vastness lay the winter constellations. Orion – his favourite – dominated the southeast, its stars more brilliant than they'd ever been before. There was Betelgeux, ruby-red. There, Rigel, glittering blue-white. There, the three stars making up Orion's belt, and below them the haze of cosmic dust that's seeded with young stars. Ahead lay the Great Bear. And there was Polaris, mysterious as the centre of a whirlpool, with all the northern star groups revolving around it.

The reindeer flew, fast and eager, until the stars faded away. The sky was dense with freezing thistledown as millions of white flakes came tumbling towards them, spiralling through the sky, sweeping past on the wind, more and more snow until it was impossible to see. Soft flakes settled on his face, hair and eyelashes, so many that Ross became a creature of snow. He felt so alive, like an animal newly born.

Even now, Ross couldn't make sense of it. Yet somehow that no longer seemed important. He stretched out, letting his head sink into the reindeer-hair pillow. Then, feeling happier than he ever thought possible, he drifted into a deep sleep.

2

The Frozen Forest

Ross slept well under the reindeer hides, enjoying his favourite dream. He was in his room under the eaves, watching the night sky, while green fire swept the darkness like a flaming torch in a giant's fist. It was always the same, although he never grew tired of it. But this time the ending was different.

Strange noises began to intrude. It sounded like scraping, then bits of wood being knocked together. There were odd smells too, which was peculiar. Ross had never dreamed smells before, neither good nor bad. Finally the dream was snatched away completely, and then things became really scary. This wasn't his bed. And something was making his head itch. Then Ross remembered. The girl. The woman. Dogs. Best not to get up straight away. He would pretend to be asleep so he could check things out.

The first thing he saw almost wrecked his plan. Looking back at him out of the gloom was a rough, ugly face. Startled by its eerie, blank expression, Ross nearly shouted out. He held his breath, waiting for it to move. But it soon became obvious that it wouldn't. It's a weird kind of doll, he thought, feeling a bit foolish – a wrinkly, dried-out, gingerbread man.

He saw that he was not in a house, but a round tent, about five metres across. Leather bags, and rolled-up rugs lay around the edge. There was an axe, a bow with some arrows, and some things that looked like old tennis rackets. Hairy clothes hung from the tent poles. Among them was his sweatshirt, a shock of blue among all those strange things.

Smoke rising from the central fire hung in a cloud up above, trying to squeeze through a hole where the tent poles met. Suspended in the smoke was a whole leg of meat. Down below, the woman knelt before the flames. She was talking to something he could not see. A kettle hissed as if in reply. There was no sign of the girl or the dogs. Ross decided to stay where he was until they came back.

He kept having flashbacks of a ride through the night, stars and snow. It didn't feel like a dream. If he'd dreamed it all, how had he got here? And where was here, anyway? It was too much of a puzzle. At least he knew that he was awake now, because he felt a strong urge to scratch his head. Just in time, he remembered he was supposed to be sleeping. Think about breakfast instead, he told himself. That's easy.

Food made him think of Mum. She must be frantic, wondering where he had gone. A quick message, no one would see. But when he reached for his phone he heard barking outside. The door was flung back, and the girl came in carrying firewood. While she took off her coat Ross sat up, making a great show of stretching.

"The sky smiles on us today," Tilda said.

Although he didn't understand, Ross grinned as if he did. The girl threw him the sweatshirt. He pulled it over his head. It was warm, and smelled of wood smoke. Then they all sat down by the fire to eat.

Breakfast was flatbread, and a strip of cold, chewy meat, washed down with tea from a wooden bowl. Ross wasn't keen on tea, especially without milk or sugar, but at least it helped the meat go down. His head still itched. He gave it a thorough scratching, sending stout hairs tumbling into his tea. He swilled them around the bowl, fascinated. His hair seemed to have gone white overnight. Was that even possible?

"When you found him," Hirta said, giving Ross a sharp look, "are you certain there was no one else there?"

"No one," Tilda replied, picking reindeer hairs from her tea. "Only him."

"That troubles me. A stranger – from where, only the Old Ones know – would never travel alone through the snow. I do not see how he got here, unless," Hirta paused to lower her voice to a whisper, "someone used the spirits to bring him."

"Who would do such a thing?"

"We know of one."

"Not him," Tilda said. "He would never do harm. He is not well enough, anyway."

Ross squirmed and fidgeted. It was boring, not knowing what they were saying. He took the phone from his pocket, and turned it on. As his face bathed in the blueish glow, Hirta and Tilda fell silent. Ross stared expectantly at the screen, too absorbed to notice how hard they were staring at him.

"What is that?" whispered Tilda.

"Foxglow," Hirta said, touching her bear's tooth. "A ray from the Wayfinders."

"Truly?"

"What else could it be?"

Tilda's eyes widened. "Imagine, catching foxglow in that ... thing."

"That thing is a scrystone," Hirta said. "I told you, there is trouble here. That lad knows things he should not."

"Not how to trap the ray. He cannot know that."

"No, of course. Skills like that take a lifetime to learn."

At that moment, Ross could have used some magic powers. He couldn't get a signal. Frowning, he turned off the phone and put it away.

"He looks sad," Tilda said, breathing normally again.

Hirta wanted to be on her own for a while, to concentrate. She had plenty to think about. "He needs to be moving, doing something. Take him with you. The forest will do the rest."

"If you are sure, Nanna."

"No need to fear the scrystone. He will not use it, he does not know how." The stranger was useless, but not dangerous, Hirta was certain. Whatever had happened was none of his doing. Anyway, Tilda had amulets sewn onto her coat, patterns of tiny beads to confuse bad spirits.

"Come on," Hirta said, "help me find some clothes."

When it came to keeping warm, reindeer knew best. Snow on a reindeer's back – even a thick layer –would never melt, because the deer's hollow hairs kept its body heat from escaping. So everything was made from reindeer skins, cut and stitched by hand, even the leggings they wore under their skirts.

The lad watched as they rummaged among the bags. Tilda found her old boots, and some well-worn leggings. She held them up for Ross to see. "He does not look keen," she said. Hirta gave an old deer-hair coat a quick shake. "He will be glad soon enough, once he is out there."

They helped the lad to put on the deerskins over his own clothes. The leggings were a struggle. It took some pushing and pulling to get them over his jeans, but at last Tilda was able to fasten the ties at his waist. Then Hirta pulled on the boots, and Tilda tied leather strips below his knees to keep them from falling down. Finally they pushed up the hood, thrust his hands into some furry mittens, and stepped back to judge the result.

"I think they will suit," Tilda said doubtfully.

"They will have to do. Keep an eye on him. Make sure he does not lose my mittens."

~

Ross lifted his arms helplessly, swamped by his clothes. The coat, which ended below his knees, wrapped right across to fasten at one side. The mittens were so loose that already they were slipping off. And there was something in the bottom of the boots that felt like stalks from some plant. How was he supposed to move in all this stuff? And why were they going outside? It was cosy in the tent. Ross did not want to go anywhere, except home.

Tilda unfastened the door, and stepped out. The dogs rushed after her, wagging their tails and barking. Somewhere a lone bell chimed softly. Then Ross felt Hirta's hands on his shoulders, pushing him through the triangular gap. The door closed behind him with a slap. He stood for a moment, confused. There was snow everywhere. And trees, lots of trees, stretching off into the darkness.

He hadn't expected it to be the middle of the night. Still half asleep, and feeling grumpy at having to go out, Ross stared down at his boots. It was weird, standing on snow in things that felt like slippers. If only he knew where he was. If only he could get on the phone. He forced himself to think. Snow. More than he had ever seen. It wasn't like the snow at home, soft, fat flakes that melted straight away, or sometimes – not for years, though – fell and fell until school was closed. This snow was different, dry and powdery. The air was biting his nose. It began to leak.

As his eyes became more used to the darkness Ross realised it wasn't totally dark. He could see reasonably well, because the snow was reflecting light from the stars. And there were billions of stars. Automatically, his gaze drifted up to Polaris –he knew exactly where it was, because he looked at it so often. To his surprise it was higher up, he was sure of it. But the pole star did not move. It couldn't, not unless he'd come north, a long way north. Maybe this was the Arctic. It was certainly cold enough.

Ross thought of the warm tent. He wondered how it looked from the outside, but with the hood pulled up he could only see straight ahead. So he shuffled the other way, and there were the dogs, frisking around the girl as she brushed snow from a sled. Next to them was the cone-shaped tent, snuggled into a low bank topped with trees. Nearby stood a wood stack – a cluster of upright branches – then a ring of tall poles bound together at the top that formed the bare bones of a second tent. Snow clung, frozen, to the bare branches of the trees, which faded away into blue shadow. Everything was washed with blue, the deep indigo of a starlit night. If this was a history re-enactment, it was the best one ever.

Felled birches formed a rough fence along the top of the bank. Behind the fence a group of reindeer was digging down through the snow. One wore a loose collar with a big square bell. Ross scanned them quickly, hoping to see his white reindeer, but they all had fawn coats and dark legs.

Tilda moved one of the poles aside, and called out to the deer. One of them came to her at once. He was a bit darker than the others, and had a blaze of white down his face. The reindeer pushed at the girl with his nose, keen to enjoy the treat she had brought.

While the reindeer chewed happily, Tilda led him out to her sled. The runners curved up at the front and there were two slim poles for shafts, which she fastened to a band around the deer's chest. The seat – lengths of wood lashed together with leather thongs – was piled with reindeer skins. "Eimross," she called, gesturing at him to climb aboard. While he settled awkwardly at the back, she threw a deerskin over his legs then jumped on in front. Immediately the reindeer set off at a fast pace, throwing Ross off balance, and as he grabbed at the backrest to steady himself, he saw the dogs trotting behind.

Although new snow had fallen the runners slid easily, cushioned by countless tiny crystals. Only the huffing of an excited reindeer, and a strange clicking from its feet, disturbed the silence of the frozen forest. It was much too quiet for Ross. No traffic rumbled in the distance, no devices hummed or chirped. With nothing to relieve it he felt the silence pressing in on him, heavy and uncomfortable. Everything seemed to be holding its breath as though expecting some terrible event. A drip formed on the end of his nose. He wiped it away with the back of Hirta's mitten and huddled down, so the fur around his hood mingled with the deerskin rug.

Irritable thoughts scratched around inside his head. Eimross. Huh! They don't even know my name. And where's the White Reindeer? I could talk to him. But he wasn't real... His thumbs itched at the thought of the phone, buried beneath layers of clothing. There was no way of reaching it at the moment.

It's never like this in movies, Ross told himself. Monsters, aliens, whatever, they're talking to you straight off, no problem. But here I can't even talk to people. These clothes stink. And they're rubbish – I'm freezing. I wish I was home. If I'm not back soon I won't get any presents. And I want to see the Northern Lights, the reindeer promised.

Self-pity was on a roll, gathering material like a runaway snowball. Ross sank further underneath the deerskin until the world was totally shut out.

If Tilda was aware of the sullen presence, she gave no sign. Nothing was allowed to spoil this. She belonged to the snowbound forest, and loved its welcoming trees, its comforting silence. As they went along she was looking out for her reindeer. If they were behaving oddly they could be ill, or a predator might be close by. Today all seemed well.

A little further on they came upon a clearing, where some of the herd were uncovering lichen by scraping the snow away with their hooves. All were females carrying next spring's calves, with this year's half-grown calves at their side. When he saw the deer the young dog set off towards them, plunging into deep snow. Larna stayed by the sled. She knew that reindeer should not be disturbed.

Tilda called out, "Fann! Here!" Excitable Fann floundered on, startling some birds that were digging for shoots buried under the snow. Rattling their alarm, the birds rose on stubby white wings, only to land again a few metres away. Fann hesitated. Which to chase, deer or birds? Shaking his head in frustration, he tried to bark through a mouthful of snow. Then Larna came up behind him, and gave Fann a nip for not obeying a command.

"Bad dog, Fann," Tilda said, doing her best to sound stern. This was a good place to build some traps. A pair of fat snow grouse would make a welcome change from deer stew.

Her sudden shout had stirred Ross from his thoughts. Despite himself, he was amused by the dogs and pushed the furs down a bit so he could see. When they set off again the sky had brightened slightly, almost enough to dull the fainter stars. For the first time he noticed the air – how it wasn't just cold, it smelt really clean. Perhaps it wasn't so bad here, after all.

It was not a dense forest, so there was space for reindeer to move between the trees. Spruces were blanketed with white, right down to the ground. Spindly birches crowded together in gangs, their branches hazed with frost and the silvery splotches on their bark glowing in the twilight. Reindeer were everywhere, heads down, digging. Ross glimpsed a small movement among the trees. It looked like a white rabbit, although he couldn't be certain.

What Ross so nearly saw was a group of hares. Invisible in their coats of winter white they watched nervously as the sled approached, standing perfectly still on their hind legs. Then one hare waggled his black-tipped ears, almost giving them all away. Once the dogs and people had passed, and all of them were safe, the hares bounded away to tell their news – a stranger was in the forest.

After what seemed a long time the trees began to thin out, and before them stretched a wide expanse of white. The reindeer stopped to snuffle in the snow. Tilda left the sled and walked to the edge, where the ground sloped down onto the snowfield. Ross followed her. While the dogs ran around them, they gazed across to the opposite bank where the forest began again. Set back among the trees was a huge white mound, with a smudge of smoke above it. "Is that an igloo? Does someone live there?" In his excitement, Ross had forgotten that she couldn't understand him.

3

The Ghost Owl

Alone in her tent, Hirta was working out what to do first. Whatever else was happening, everyday tasks always needed to be done. If they were to eat that night then she would have to make a start.

As she prepared dough for the bread, Hirta considered their food supplies. With the herd close by there was no shortage of meat. But those deer had been chosen at leaf fall, and she did not want to lose any more. The other things, the little luxuries, had been carefully calculated to last out the long night. So if the lad were to stay, rations that had been enough for two would have to be split three ways. "Cutting down on bread would be hard," she muttered, as she laid out portions of dough to bake on the hearthstones. "And tea, imagine going without tea. Unthinkable."

Hirta unhooked the cooking pot from its chain above the fire, and set it down on the floor. That stew would have made another meal if it had not been for the stranger. With a heavy sigh she took up her knife, and began to chop and slice. Into the pot went starchy roots, strips of meat and dried berries, with herbs for extra flavour. She added some water from the kettle, leaving enough to top up the cooking pot, and make a brew of tea. Rationing could start later. Once done, she heaved the cauldron back onto the hook, and knelt down beside the fire.

One of the hearthstones was much shinier than the others, the result of years of polishing. It was by far the oldest thing in the tent, even older than the wooden guardian. Hirta reached out, and stroked the hot stone as if it were a pet. "Keeper of the hearth, be welcome," she said. "Keep away the cold and darkness, keep away the ache of hunger, keep away all harm this day."

A surge from the flames sent sparks up among the smoke. Something like hot air was shimmering above the shiny stone. Hirta nodded a greeting. "Help me, firesprite. If you know anything about the stranger, tell me."

The firesprite stopped flickering, as though it had been switched off. Then it brightened up again. "Your visitor, you mean?"

"Yes. The lad. Where are his kinfolk? What is he doing here?"

"He is not from the forest."

"I know that," Hirta said, crossly. They had shared so much and kept nothing from each other, at least so far as she was aware. Now the firesprite knew more than it was prepared to say. It was an uncomfortable reminder that this was not a friendship between equals. "You are supposed to know things. Things beyond my understanding." Hirta was surprised by her own words. It was not wise to be disrespectful to a hearth-keeper.

The firesprite assumed a coy expression. "Some things even I do not know," it said, adding slyly, "I am only a domestic sprite, after all."

They stared at each other for a moment. Fuelled by worry and frustration, Hirta's temper began to boil. Surely it knew. Why would it not tell her?

"I do know something," the firesprite said. "That stew is about to burn."

Hirta swore under her breath. She leapt up to examine the cauldron. More water was needed at once. Grabbing the deerskin potholder to protect her hand, she lifted up the kettle. It felt far too light.

"Empt-eee, empt-eee," the firesprite chirped, in an irritating tone.

Hirta had a feeling that it had done this on purpose, to stop her from asking any more questions. Furious, she threw the potholder at the tiny figure. The deerskin sizzled and ignited with a flash. The firesprite disappeared, and the flames from the fire went down low.

There was nothing for it but to go outside for some ice. Hirta was reaching for her mittens when she remembered they were not in their usual place. The lad was wearing them. "What a nuisance he is," she muttered, grasping the naked handle of the kettle. "Ow!" Wincing from the sting of hot metal, she cursed her wandering thoughts. She picked up the kettle, this time using a handful of skirt.

Outside, Hirta pressed her palm into the snow, and held it there to cool the burn. The freezing sensation calmed her quickly. What had she been thinking of, to speak in such a way to the hearth keeper? Their safety, and comfort, depended on its goodwill. A disgruntled firesprite could cause all kinds of mischief. Had she really thrown something at it? She cringed at the memory. "Here less than a day, that lad, and already causing trouble."

Shaking her numb hand, Hirta headed for the ice heap. She hacked at it with her knife, and threw bits into the big kettle until it was full to the top. Lake ice was purer than snow, but neither made as much water as you thought, once it was melted. She would have to come out again before long. With both hands now red from the cold, Hirta clasped the kettle to her chest, and fled back inside to the warmth. She had offended the firesprite and must make amends.

~

Tilda stared across the frozen lake to the hut on the opposite bank. Her sharp eyes, accustomed to distance, allowed her to see further than Ross even in the twilight.

Everything looked normal at their neighbour's camp. The woodstack was well stocked, and filleted fish were freeze-drying on the rack. She was glad to see that he was looking after himself. Sometimes she would call on Rymi to ask if there was anything he needed, but not today. Not with the stranger here.

As she took in the scene there was a movement in the woods. Like a layer of snow sliding over snow, it was so subtle that the stranger did not notice. A white wolf had slipped out from among the trees, and was standing in front of the hut, watching them.

Larna noticed. Wolves killed reindeer, so she was on alert. At the sight of the enemy her neck hair stiffened, and a low rumbling began in her throat.

"All right, lass." Tilda knew this wolf. It was Rymi's companion, befriended by him one unusually hard winter. At the time, Nanna had plenty to say about it. "He should know better, bringing a wolf into camp. What about the deer? And that one is clever. It has found a man to protect it." Yet Tilda was sympathetic. She had seen how the wolf was company for Rymi, who treated it like a dog. In return, the young wolf seemed to share its master's mind. If the wolf was on guard then he did not want visitors.

Suddenly something soft struck her shoulder, then trickled down her back. Tilda turned to see the lad, grinning, his hands cupping a small heap of snow. She didn't respond. She was used to being alone, moving carefully and quietly, so as not to disturb anything without good reason. The stranger did not understand. Behaviour like his could spoil their luck with the fish. But at least he was not so moody, which was an improvement.

Now there was work to be done. Without a word Tilda returned to the sled, while Ross stared, blank-faced. What was wrong with her? Everybody liked a snowball fight, even if the stuff was too powdery to stick properly. And what was the use of all this space, if you couldn't have fun? She's weird, he decided, bashing the mittens together to shed the last of the snow. Meanwhile, Tilda had collected a deerskin bag and was walking down the bank. Ross hesitated, wondering whether he should follow. A quick glance around confirmed there was nothing else to do, so he scrambled down after her.

Tilda stopped beside a tree branch that was lying in the snow. As she picked it up, Ross saw a thin line leading from the branch into a hollow beneath. Pulling a knife from her belt, she knelt to tease out the packing of pine needles that prevented the hole from freezing up. With the plug removed, water welled up into the gap.

For the first time it occurred to Ross that this was not solid ground. A river – maybe a lake – lay under their feet, and only a layer of frozen water was keeping them from falling in. If the ice cracked, they might not make it to the bank.

Untroubled by such thoughts, Tilda took off her mittens, and grasped the line. Slowly, she began to draw it from the water. Suddenly, in a flick of spray, a silvery-grey fish appeared. As it hung, gasping, Tilda removed the hook and killed the fish by striking its head on the ice. She pulled out more line. Soon another fish lay next to the first. Then she turned to Ross, and offered him the fishing line.

Ross bent over the ice hole. Without the warm mittens his hands became clumsy, and he wondered how the girl could manage with frozen fingers. Yet he persevered, until finally an even larger fish was dangling from the line, thrashing its tail. The girl clapped. Ross gave her a wry grin. His first ever fish. But nobody would know because he couldn't get on the phone.

Tilda was pleased. Three good fish, and the stranger had helped willingly. Perhaps he had fishing luck after all. She gave thanks to her forebears, who put skill into her hands. And thanks to the water spirits who sent fish to her line.

At her lookout post on the bank Larna stood up, stretched, and with a last glance at the wolf, barked an alarm. She was telling them to head home, because the brief twilight was darkening. Tilda pushed the packing back into the hole, rolled up the fishing line, and started across the ice. The stranger followed, carrying the bag of fish.

Tilda had decided to let him drive back. In truth, he would only think that he was driving – her reindeer knew the way so well he needed no guidance. She loaded the sled and called the lad's name, "Eimross." The stranger looked surprised to be seated at the front. He was even more surprised when she put the reins into his hands. Tilda knelt down behind him, called out to the reindeer, and the sled started to move.

The reindeer ran swiftly, making excited grunts. Ross had nothing to do except feel rather pleased with himself. He had caught some fish, and now he was in charge of a sled. It was really moving. All the reindeer's feet seemed to be in the air at the same time.

Ross was thinking this is more like it, when something swooped out of the trees right in front of the reindeer. Silent, ghostly, it was there, and then it was gone. The startled reindeer shook his antlers then bolted along the track, while the dogs ran alongside, barking frantically. Behind them the sled swung wildly, out of control. Ross dropped the reins so he could hang on to the seat. Tilda stretched around him to grab them, but the reins were flapping just out of her reach. Her shouts went unheeded. The reindeer refused to stop. Risking injury, she dug a heel into the snow. That was no use either. It didn't slow the sled one bit.

Ross stared at the plunging legs right in front of his eyes. Who knew reindeer could go so fast? But the thrill was soon over. One of the runners hit a tree root. Instantly the back of the sled flipped up, and everything on it was thrown through the air. Narrowly missing a tree, Ross landed in deep snow along with the bag of fish, and a scattering of reindeer pelts.

Tilda was on her feet at once. After a quick look to see that he was alive she ran off down the track, calling after the dogs and the disappearing reindeer.

Ross sat up too soon. The forest was spinning, and so was his head. Woody giants waved too many arms. Twigs crawled through churning snow. The fish, wriggling and thrashing in their bag, threatened to burst it wide open. Ross groaned. Holding his head to stop it falling off, he shut his eyes, and willed it all to stop. Miraculously, this worked. Once more the bag was just a bag of dead fish.

He was busy poking snow out of his ears when something caught his eye, a dark shape in the snow among the deer hides. He crawled over to investigate. It was nothing, just a cone from a tree. But as he stared at it, Ross saw how

25

perfect it was – special enough to keep. He checked the coat for pockets in all the usual places, yet found none. He picked the cone up anyway.

"Well, look who's here. Enjoy the trip, stranger?"

Ross knew that voice. Quickly, he pushed the cone into his hood, and waited for the white reindeer to appear. Instead a huge, grey bird came gliding out of the trees. It settled, without a sound, on a nearby branch.

"Who're you?" Ross said, not bothering to hide his disappointment. "Where's the white reindeer?"

"Hooo-hooo, hoo-hoo-hoo."

If a ghost tried to laugh, Ross thought, that's exactly how it would sound – silly and sinister at the same time. But this wasn't a ghost. It wasn't a normal owl, either. Bands of feathers, dark grey and pale grey, encircled an enormous face. Fierce white eyebrows lurched above yellow eyes. Bunches of white feathers sprouted around its beak, like false whiskers that weren't fixed on properly. Ross had a nervous urge to laugh. Then, for a terrible instant, the face became *human*. No, of course it didn't – just another trick of the twilight.

"Have we met?" the grey owl said, shifting from foot to foot.

Ross frowned. That was the white reindeer's voice, and yet… "It was you!" he said. "You made us crash."

"Hooo-hooo, no other way to meet you."

"This place is weird. Animals talk, and they all sound the same."

The owl seemed to find this hilarious. "Hooo-hooo, hoo–hoo-hoo. Hooo-hooo, hoo-hoo-hoo." It laughed so much it overbalanced, and almost tipped off the branch. "Be serious," it told itself, straightening up, and re-folding its long wings. "You must be ready, stranger. Soon the Wayfinders will come. Their torches will light up the sky."

"Torches? You mean the Northern Lights?"

The owl fluffed out its feathers in a kind of shrug.

"I'm going to see the Lights!"

"Not only that," the owl said. "The Wayfinders can help you."

"How? Will they get me home?"

The owl seemed pleased by that. "Going home would be wise. There is nothing for you here. So-ooo, when their torches come, call to them. Like this." The owl stretched up until it became tall and thin. "Fyooo-fyooo, fyoo-fyoo. You try."

Ross tried. He wasn't much good at whistling, let alone whistling like an owl.

"Again. You can do better."

Ross was not convinced, yet he carried on until his head was light enough to float away. At last the owl was satisfied. "You did well," it said. "Whistle like that, and the Wayfinders will come to you. Come right down. Tell them what you want, and so it will be."

Along the track came the faint swishing of runners. The grey owl turned its face towards the sound, bowed slightly, and rose on silent wings. "Do-ooo it, doo it," it called. "Tell them you want to go home."

4

The Wayfinders

It had taken Tilda some time to catch up with her racing reindeer. Determined to reach the safety of the herd, he did not stop until his reins became snagged on a low-hanging branch. "I should thank that tree," she told him, "it can move faster than me."

After his frantic dash the runaway was much too hot. To add to his discomfort he was made to retrace his steps. The reindeer plodded along reluctantly, trying to cool down by letting his long tongue flop out. Tilda was in no mood to hurry him as she was in a similar state, burning up inside her warm clothes. Only Larna and Fann had enjoyed the incident. The dogs padded beside the sled, bright-eyed and laughing, certain their efforts had halted the reindeer.

When she arrived at the scene of the accident Tilda found the stranger sitting in the snow. He had not moved, not even to gather up the deer hides. She tethered her reindeer to a birch, and hurried over. The lad was gazing into the forest, looking so happy that Tilda feared he'd hit his head. "Eimross? Are you hurt?" There was no reply. She took hold of his hood to cover his head, but first she had to tip out some snow, twigs, and an old spruce cone. The lad looked up, surprised, as if he had just noticed she was there. Words spilled out, accompanied by wild gestures. He was all right, after all.

As they piled everything back onto the sled a grating croak came down from the sky, *kraa, kraa, kraa*. Ice trickled down Tilda's spine. Raven did not flee the snow like most other birds – he stayed throughout the long night, telling tales to the forest spirit.

~

Hirta was sitting beside the fire, sewing. It had been easier than she expected to soothe the firesprite. A special little flatbread, left on the shiny stone, had been enough to pacify it. The firesprite had appeared unbidden, and was behaving as though nothing unusual had happened. Pushing any lingering doubts to the back of her mind, Hirta gripped a length of sinew between her front teeth, pulled it so the end became flat, and then fed it through the eye of the bone needle.

A search through a bag of deerskin pieces had turned up an old pair of mittens. One was ripped across the back, and just needed a patch. On the other, the seam around the thumb had come unstitched. They would not take long to repair. As she worked Hirta talked, knowing the firesprite would be listening.

"Is it worth taking the lad to the settlement? Someone might recognise his speech. Then we would know his kinfolk." Hirta did not relish that journey at the moment. The snow was still too soft. "Would that help, though? They will not know any more than I do. And some there are against the old ways. It would bring trouble if they got to hear." Hirta knotted the thread, and severed it with her knife. "What a thing to do, bring someone on a spirit journey. I once heard talk, but never knew it done."

Glancing at the fire out of the corner of her eye, she noticed the hearth-keeper. It was creeping from stone to stone, taking a bite out of each portion of bread. "Whoever did it knew what they were about," she said, pretending not to notice. "It will take someone as skilled to put all to rights. Until then the lad will have to stay." Hirta held up her sewing to examine the repairs. "They will serve. It will be good to have my mittens back."

~

Tilda drove for the rest of their journey. Ross sat behind her clutching the bag of fish, with Fann laid across his legs. The young dog was tired, so Tilda had allowed him to ride on the sled.

Ross was watching the stars. Every moment, more appeared. There were so many, far more than he had ever seen at home, crowding the constellations until he struggled to recognise them. To rest his eyes he focussed instead on the tops of the trees. Between their branches something was stirring – a flowing scarf of milky-white silk. "Look!" Ross yelled. "It's the Lights." Startled, Tilda stopped the sled. Nearby was a clearing among the trees, where snow sparkled as if under a full moon. They watched the scarf creep further up the sky, its lazily drifting ends now fringed with green. Ross could wait no longer. Abandoning both dog and bag, he leapt from the sled and ran into the clearing. Tilda followed cautiously. Boulders and branches hid under snow, creating traps to injure careless feet.

Face upturned, Ross was consumed by the unfolding spectacle. Waves were dancing along the scarf, pulses of light coming faster and faster. The scarf formed an arch that split into two. One half twirled, sending green rays high into the sky. This was it. This was his chance to go home.

Ross thought of the owl, and tried to whistle. He couldn't make a sound. Take a deep breath, he told himself. Try harder. "Fyooo, fyooo, fyoo, fyoo." Incredibly, the lights paused. Ross whistled again. Now the rays were grouping into columns, closing into folds. Like gigantic curtains hemmed with pink, they began their slow descent.

A little way behind him Tilda stopped, touching the amulet she wore at her neck. Ross stared, mesmerised, as the veils of light edged closer. If he reached out now he could touch them, for sure.

Tell them what you want, and so it will be.

"I wish…I…" Ross hesitated, suddenly aware of the unimaginable power hanging above his head. In that moment words rushed to fill the blank space in his mind. Before he knew it, they were spoken. "I wish I could talk to the girl. And her Gran."

A universe of singing voices filled his head. Every nerve crackled, and burned. When he felt that he could bear it no longer, that he was going to pass out, the sensations stopped. The glowing curtain lifted. Higher and higher it went, hastening away in showers of red and green.

Ross was left dazed. The snow was blue again, and the sky blue-black, except for a faint trace where the aurora had been. He heard the rustle of soft boots in snow, and felt Tilda's hand on his arm. "We must go," she said.

What was that? *We must go.* It had worked. "Did you see? Brilliant. Amazing."

Tilda moved her hand away. "You speak our tongue."

"No, um, not really."

"You do. You did it again."

"No, it's you. You're speaking English."

"I am not. All this time you were pretending."

"I wasn't, honest. It wasn't like that. Really." Ross waved

a hand at the sky. "They did it, the Lights. They made it so we could talk."

"You called the spirits…"

Ross shrugged. "They did what I asked, like the owl said."

Tilda had heard of people whistling down the Wayfinders, asking them to grant a wish. Just firelight talk, she used to think. "How did you dare? They could have hurt you, killed you."

"Like I said, the grey owl told me what to do. You'd run off after the sled. Anyway, it worked, didn't it?"

Tilda had seen no grey owl, only heard the call of a raven. But her own eyes had seen the stranger summon the Wayfinders. "The sky is calm now," she said softly. "Nanna will have our meal ready."

~

Back at the tent, there was so much to explain that their catch was almost forgotten. "These are fine fish," Hirta said, as the firelight glinted on their smooth, golden bellies. "We will keep them for breakfast." So their meal that night was stew again.

"Thanks," Ross said, setting down his empty bowl. "That was good."

Tilda frowned at his small lie. The stew was burnt, anyone could tell. And Nanna had left the bread too long – one side was charred. That was a bad omen.

"Glad you enjoyed it, young stranger," Hirta said. Ross thought he should be polite, so he said something he'd heard Mum say to his Gran. "What was in it?"

"Oh, the usual," Hirta replied. "Roots, berries, and reindeer meat."

Ross felt a bit queasy. He wished he hadn't asked. "You eat reindeer?"

"Why, yes," Hirta said. "Do folk not eat meat where you come from?"

"Suppose so." Ross had never thought about what went into his favourite sausages, but he thought about it now.

"We could have snow grouse," Tilda said. "They are in the forest, we saw some near the lake. Fann tried to catch one."

Hirta beamed. She was well versed in forest lore, and seldom missed a chance to share it. "When snowbirds feed on mountain side, winter will not blow so wild. When snowbirds feed among the trees, count your logs against a freeze." She chuckled. "Silly, I know. But a true thing."

Tilda sighed. "We have enough wood. Our hearth will not grow cold."

"Yes, Old Ones be thanked," Hirta said. "Now then, young stranger," she turned to Ross. "Tell us all about yourself."

"Eimross, Nanna. His name is Eimross."

"No it's not," Ross said.

"No?" Tilda looked hurt. "What is it then?"

"It's Ross. Just Ross."

"You could have said before."

No I couldn't, Ross thought. He grinned at them nervously. Where to start? Would they believe him? He wasn't sure if he believed it himself. So he began by telling them about his loft bedroom, and the sloping ceiling with a window set into it that looked out towards the north. It was perfect for viewing the Northern Lights, except they couldn't usually be seen from where he lived.

"But sometimes it's possible. When there's a big storm on the sun, loads of stuff blasts towards Earth and charges up the atmosphere over the North Pole. If it's a big geomagnetic storm you can see the Lights from lots of places." He wasn't sure they understood that. But when he described the white reindeer on the roof, and how it spoke to him, they exchanged knowing glances. "Then it gets a bit mixed up," he said. "I think we were flying to the pole star. Only I might have dreamed that bit."

"That was no dream, young stranger," Hirta said, her face solemn. "Beneath the Steadfast star is a great tree, invisible to our eyes. It holds up the sky, as these poles hold up our tent." She gestured at the place where the poles met. "Up there, see how the smoke goes out through that hole? They say there is a hole near Steadfast, where spirits pass into the upper world."

She seemed about to say something else, although Ross was relieved when she didn't. He was more confused than ever. In the uneasy silence that followed he found himself thinking about Grandad. He'd felt so excited when that message arrived, the aurora alert. He wanted to tell someone. Not Mum and Dad, they were always busy. He wanted to tell Grandad.

They used to do things, have a laugh – a kickabout, or Grandad's favourite, snakes and ladders. It was Grandad who'd got him interested in space, talking about the moonbase and the plans for Mars, and how the first human footprints were still out there in the moon's dust. "Everyone who ever lived looked at that moon and those stars," he used to say. "Now it's your turn." Together they would watch the space station go over, like a golden spark gliding from west to east. Then Grandad would name a planet, and challenge Ross to find it.

So Grandad understood about the aurora. But he couldn't talk to Grandad, not now. Not ever. Ross scratched his head in frustration. It was a habit that really annoyed his Mum, but how are you supposed to stop doing something when you don't even know you're doing it?

Hirta watched, grim-faced. He had better not have lops. And why was there no mention of his parents? Perhaps they had trodden the path of souls. "The scrystone," she said, "who gave you that?" The lad looked puzzled. "The black stone, with foxglow inside. You held it up like this," Hirta held her hand palm upwards in front of her face, "and the light shone out."

"Oh. You mean this," Ross said, taking out the phone.

"Yes, that. It is very special. You are lucky to have it." Hirta grasped her bear-tooth amulet for comfort. "Who gave it to you?"

Ross shrugged. "Mum."

So, thought Hirta, his Ma still lives. And she is skilled in spiritcraft. Perhaps she was the one who sent him.

"Will it do anything you want?" Tilda asked.

"Almost anything." Odd that they'd never seen a phone before. "And you can talk to anyone, anywhere in the world. I'll show you."

Hirta was impressed. The lad's mother had great knowledge. She had given her son the power to send his thoughts through the air. She watched him with some unease, in case he was skilful enough to be a threat. Yet as soon as the light showed he shut it off again.

"Something wrong?" Tilda asked.

"I can't do it now."

"The light has escaped," Hirta said. "Gone back to the sky."

Ross made an ugly face to hide his fear. "Don't be stupid. Needs charging, that's all."

Hirta had to bite her tongue. The lad did not understand what a treasure he had. Nor did he know how it worked, that was obvious.

"Nanna is helping you," Tilda said. "She does not deserve harsh words."

Ross glared at the useless gadget, the friend that had let him down. Until now, he'd thought everything would be all right. His dream had come true, he'd seen the Northern Lights, and they were better than he ever imagined. Now he could go home. But how could anyone find him? They didn't know where he was. He didn't know where he was. Without the phone he was stuck. Helpless. "Sorry," he said grudgingly.

"All is well, young stranger," Hirta replied through gritted teeth. Then she saw his eyes flash in surprise.

"Here, look," Ross said, grinning. "That flame looks like a goblin, or something." He jabbed a finger towards the fire. "See? There. It's yawning."

Hirta sat motionless, aghast. Why did it show itself now, to him? She never laughed at the hearth-keeper. It would take offence. The firesprite would leave, and never come back.

"Can't you see?" Ross said. "Now it's–"

"We know," Tilda said, "but we do not speak of it. Or point at it," she added, hastily. "It is forbidden. Disrespectful."

Just then the firesprite took hold of the corners of its mouth, and stretched them right back to its ears. From this grotesque mask a long tongue of fire shot out like a flamethrower, making Ross start backwards.

When he looked again it was gone. He must have imagined it. Yet it had seemed so real. Not for the first time, Ross was afraid of this strange place. Then a terrible thought struck him. Stupid! Why hadn't he asked the Lights to take him home, when he had the chance? "It's hopeless," he said. "I'll never get home now."

"You will, young stranger. I know someone who can help." Hirta was feeling more kindly now he couldn't use the scrystone.

"Has he got a charger?" Ross asked hopefully. "Or a snowmobile?"

"Certainly not," Hirta said, although she had no idea what they were. "Look what I have got for you. New mittens. Go on, try them." Reluctantly, Ross pulled them on. They smelt funny, and looked a bit tatty, but at least they were a better fit than the ones he'd been wearing.

"Oh, look at Fann," Tilda said. "He wants to play."

The dog crouched, his front legs stretched out, and bottom in the air. The fluffy tail, arched over his back, waved happily to signal his intent. Ross reached out a furry hand. Fann pounced, seizing it firmly between sharp, white teeth. Hirta watched as they tugged the mitten back and forth. She hoped more repairs would not be needed. "Tomorrow we will visit the one who sees. Then all will be well."

Later, as he lay on the mattress of twigs, Ross planned his escape. He would creep out, harness the reindeer, and then take off through the forest. It was a good plan, except for one problem. He didn't know which way to go. Would he find the owl or the white reindeer? What else might be out there in the darkness?

Ross opened his eyes. Golden firelight was flickering across the walls of the tent. He pulled the warm deer hides around him, and let his eyelids close. There was enough charge for one call, at least. Anyway, Tilda and her Gran were doing their best. Whatever happened, he'd just have to go along with it.

5

One Who Sees

"W here are we?" Ross asked Tilda.

"In the forest. Near the lake."

This wasn't much help. He tried something else. "Is this where you live? All the time?"

"Only in the long night," she replied. "We move around. Follow the reindeer."

"Why?"

"Well," Tilda explained patiently, "they need food. Now it is lichen they eat, from under the snow. In the long day there is no snow – then they eat leaves, and grass. When they finish in one place they move on. We go where they go."

"What for?"

Tilda frowned. "What strange things you ask. We are reindeer folk. We look after them. They look after us." Ross considered that. "You can't have a proper home, then." Tilda gave him a pitying look. "Home goes with us, wherever we go. It is here, always," and she placed a hand over her heart.

Tilda was harnessing up the reindeer from the day before. His coat was dark fawn, with chocolate-brown legs, and a long, pale beard at his throat. "This is Miri,' she said, stroking his white face. "His Ma died soon after he was born, so I took care of him. Now he thinks I am his Ma."

While they were talking there was a commotion in the pen, where the group of draught animals was milling around. Hirta was trying to separate one deer from the rest. She was not having much success. The wily old reindeer had not been in harness for a while, and had no intention of being caught.

"Nanna needs help," Tilda said, handing Miri's reins to Ross. "Hold him, while I catch Olli." A lasso of plaited sinew lay draped across her chest, slung from one shoulder. With one quick movement it was in her hand.

"Can I stroke him?" Ross asked.

Tilda nodded. "Not his antlers, though. That annoys them."

Left alone with Miri, Ross gripped the reins tightly. He hoped nothing unusual would happen as he took off a mitten, and slowly stretched out his hand. Miri rolled his dark eyes backwards, yet did not move. Ross laid his hand on the reindeer's shoulder as gently as he could. The thick hair was whisper-soft and springy, like a cushion of moss.

At that moment Hirta sent Larna to turn back the dodging reindeer, so Ross turned to watch. Tilda was waiting, holding loops of lasso in her right hand, with the rest in her left. As Olli came past her she threw the lasso so it fell slightly in front of him, catching one antler. Tilda pulled on the cord, bracing herself against the deer's weight. Once he realised that he was caught, Old Olli stopped struggling and became calm. He was an odd-looking reindeer, with a white ring around each eye.

He looks funny, Ross thought. Like he's wearing glasses. He'd forgotten about the reindeer he was holding, so when Miri began to shake his head it took him by surprise. Ross jumped back quickly, out of range of the waving antlers. There was an ominous crack. In slow motion, or so it appeared, one of Miri's antlers toppled off his head, and landed in the snow, upside-down.

Ross stared at the lop-sided reindeer, wondering what to do. Miri gazed back, unconcerned. In place of his antler he sported a red-raw patch. Now Tilda was returning, rewinding her lasso. Ross scrambled for something to say. "It wasn't me, honest. I never touched it."

Tilda laughed. She put one arm through the gathered loops, and pulled the lasso over her head. "That always happens around now."

"Oh. I thought they, like, had them all the time."

"You know so little."

"Because we don't have reindeer," Ross said, indignantly.

Tilda was quiet for a moment, reflecting on the prospect of a life without reindeer. "That is very sad. But you will learn. Bulls lose their antlers first, after the rut. Then sled deer like Miri. The cows keep theirs till after they have calved. Then they all grow some more. New antlers every year." She bent down to retrieve the antler from the snow. "This we keep, for lasso practise."

~

When their sleds arrived at the edge of the lake they did not stop, but carried on down the uneven bank and out onto the ice. As they headed across at a steady pace Hirta leaned forward to peer at her friend's camp. "No wolf. I am glad of that," she said.

"He will be near," Tilda replied. "He was yesterday. I saw him watching us."

"A wolf? I never saw it," Ross muttered.

"You know what Fa used to say," Hirta said. "Never let a wolf see your soft belly."

"I know, Nanna, but this one is friendly."

Hirta snorted. "A wolf is nobody's friend."

Once the sleds were drawn up on the other bank, Tilda secured the reindeer while her grandmother set the dogs to guard them. While they were busy, Ross examined the camp.

On one side bare tent poles rose starkly from the snow, with the shapes of buried sledges close by. On the other side stood the domed hut. Now he could see that it wasn't an igloo, because twigs were poking through its covering of snow. Beside the door lay a saucer-shaped stone containing smouldering embers.

"That is for us," Hirta said, coming up behind him. "We take hair from our clothes and burn it, to protect the sacred space. Nothing bad must enter."

"If that's for us, how did he know we were coming?" Ross asked.

Tilda smiled. "He sees everything."

"Now listen, young stranger," Hirta said. "Rymi is a good man, so show some respect. Do as we do. No talking unless he speaks to you first."

As the others dropped their hairs into the saucer, Ross tugged at the fur trim on his hood until a tuft came out. He dropped it onto the glowing woodchips, watching as the hair writhed in the heat. Smoke stung his nose with a sharp medicinal scent. It reminded him of when he had a bad cold, and Gran made him sit with a towel over his head, breathing in fumes from a steaming bowl.

"We are here," Hirta called, stamping her feet to remove any snow. "And we bring a visitor." Although the answering voice was barely audible, she pulled open the door. Ross craned his neck to see inside. A damped-down fire in the centre of the hut gave a dim, reddish light, by which he could see someone sitting on the floor. Nobody spoke as they filed in to wait at a respectful distance.

Four large reindeer antlers stood around the hearth. To one side lay a reindeer pelt, white as a fresh drift of snow, and on it sat Rymi, cross-legged, his head bowed. He was draped in a long coat, also of white deerskin, laden with amulets, small bells, and leather tassels. Around his leather cap ran a circlet of copper, from which sprang a set of copper antlers. In his left hand he held a shallow, oval drum.

The two herders settled down opposite him. Ross remained standing, staring, until Tilda seized his arm and made him sit down. He sneaked a look at Hirta and Tilda, and saw their faces shining with excitement. He was beginning to feel it too.

Just as Ross was wondering when something was going to happen, Rymi took up a stick, and struck the drum loudly. For a while he beat a slow rhythm. Then the sound began to speed up. The man swayed from side to side, each beat marked by jangling amulets. The pace grew faster until it was irresistible. Soon the three of them were swaying too. Then the rhythm eased, and the mood became calmer. Once they were all still again, Rymi raised his head, and began to sing.

Storms in the mountains, lakes locked in ice, creatures of the forest, all were alive in Rymi's voice. The song stirred ancient memories Ross didn't know he had. To hear it was to know the dreams of sleeping wolves, or the secret flowing of streams under snow. Hirta and Tilda joined in with some parts. Ross was too embarrassed, even if he'd known how. He had never heard anyone sing like that, soaring high and low without even taking a breath. Yet strange though it was, there was something familiar about that voice.

Now Rymi called on his strongest spirit. He described its blue eyes, its majestic antlers, its iridescent coat. He told how this marvellous beast had helped him on his journeys in other worlds. And how, at this very moment, it was on its way to join them.

At this point the drumming fell to a soft roll. Wild cries from unseen birds whirled around their heads. From out of the shadows came the huffing of a reindeer, and the clicking of its heels. Ross felt his heart thumping. Was this his white reindeer? The sounds came towards them, and then seemed to move around the hut, rising high above their heads. Birds shrieked and mewed yet there was nothing to be seen. Finally Rymi threw back his head and his mouth fell open. The animal sounds ceased. For a while he remained in a trance, drumming ever more slowly. Then, lowering his head, he put down the drum with a shaking hand.

Ross hardly knew what to think. This was so unlike anything he had experienced. He continued to watch the man who, only a moment ago, had been so full of energy – now he looked exhausted. His eyes were almost closed, and his shoulders drooped under the weight of the coat.

A few heartbeats later, Hirta stood up. Taking care not to tread on the white deerskin she picked up a pipe that lay nearby, and examined the bowl to make sure it was filled. She lit a twig at the fire, put the long stem in her mouth, and applied the flame, drawing in air until the leaves were glowing satisfactorily. Finally Hirta puffed out a cloud of smoke, and then handed the pipe to Rymi. He took it without a word.

"Rymi needs to rest," she said, clearing her throat. "I will stay with him. You two go, and check on the dogs. Quietly, now."

~

It was good to be in the fresh air away from the smoking pipe, although Ross felt light-headed now he was outside. "What was all that about?" he asked, trying to make it sound as though he didn't care.

Tilda was so thrilled by their experience that she didn't notice his tone. "Rymi is very powerful," she said. "He knows many songs. When the door to the other world opened, and the bird spirits came, and the reindeer..."

Ross scratched his head. Doubts were dampening his excitement, although it had seemed real enough at the time. "I thought that was my white reindeer. What was it then? A ghost? Or him doing magic tricks?"

"You were there. You heard it. Felt it."

"It wasn't real though, was it?"

"How can you say that?" Tilda turned on him, face flushed with indignation. "How do you think you came here? What about the Wayfinders? They are real. You talked to them. And you saw our firesprite, I know you did."

The force of her emotion made Ross uneasy. He took a kick at the snow, spraying it into the air. "It's weird, this place. There's spirits everywhere."

"Yes! The trees have spirits – they are listening now. Animals, water, fire, even the rocks, all have spirits. The snow also."

Ross looked at the scoop he'd made in the snow. He remembered what he had seen after he was thrown off the sled. Was that spirits? Or just something that happens when you hurt your head?

"Look at them," Tilda said, gesturing at the dogs. "They are ordered to guard the deer against wolves." When he saw her looking at him, Fann stood up as if he intended to move. Then he remembered he shouldn't, and sat down again. "See?" she said. "They will not move until they are

44

told, however long it takes. They trust us to know what is right." Tilda frowned. "You are so suspicious, you do not trust your own senses."

~

"Feeling better?" Hirta asked.

Rymi's reply came wrapped in pale smoke. "Unlikely. I have seen too many winters." He noticed her eyeing the fire, and knew what she was thinking. "If you must, a couple only. Too much heat is unwelcome."

"The gift is still with you," Hirta said. She chose the two fattest logs in the heap, and placed them carefully, so as not to disturb his hearth-keeper.

"It brings weariness, nothing but weariness. So much sleeping, I may never wake." There was silence, as both of them stared at the fresh logs. Then suddenly Rymi smiled. "No more grumbling. A good friend is here. My heart is glad."

"I meant to come sooner," Hirta said, pushing back her cap to reveal a wave of iron-grey hair, "but there is always so much to do." She knelt by the fire less gracefully than she intended. Lately, everything seemed more of an effort. "We need your help, for the lad."

Rymi nodded. "Our young stranger. Where are his kinfolk?"

"That is a mystery. Tilda found him lying in the snow. He says a white reindeer took him to Steadfast – I think his Ma sent him. She must be skilled in spiritcraft, because she gave him a scrystone that shines with foxglow. He knows nothing of such things. Now he is stranded here." Hirta paused, scrutinising her friend's face. Years of extreme weather had deepened the work of time, leaving him with a sombre expression that gave nothing away. But then, he had always been careful about sharing his thoughts. "I think you know all this," she said. "The white deer is your soul kin."

Hirta knew she had said too much because he showed no sign of answering. She longed for a bowl of tea – her tongue felt like a dried toadstool – and she wondered if she should fill the kettle, or if that would offend the hearth-keeper as much as she had offended Rymi. But she had mistaken his mood. When he spoke, his manner was thoughtful.

"The journey is ending for me. Soon I will go into the hill."

"Oh, Rymi, not yet."

"I have seen it, Hirta. There is nothing to fear. Nothing. Except... I failed to pass on the craft."

She gasped. If he died before he could train an apprentice, Rymi could never enter the upper world. All his knowledge would be lost. His souls would have to wander for eternity.

"I searched all the worlds for someone to help me," he said sadly. "You know how it is here. Our folk have lost their ease with the old ways."

"Is that why the stranger came? To be your apprentice?"

Rymi looked away. "That was a mishap," he said briskly, fingering the carvings on the pipe. Hirta knew this was difficult to admit. Those who see never made an error, or at least, never confessed to one. "The reindeer spirit was strong," he continued, "and I was weary." There was nothing Hirta could think of to say, so she sighed sympathetically. He looked up, and met her gaze. "We grow old, you and I," Rymi said softly. "We can struggle against the blizzard, yet all is white silence in the end."

"A true thing, and no mistake," she agreed.

"The seeing was unclear," he said, wincing at the memory. "As blurred as peering through ice. It was a place of lonely souls, hungry souls, all seeking something. Then one stood out from the rest. Someone was dreaming of the Wayfinders. It must be one of us, that was my thought." Rymi inhaled the calming smoke. "So my soul kin brought the wrong person. That lad can never be my apprentice."

"You will find someone."

"There will not be time."

"But, surely–"

"It is over," Rymi said. "My last chance, gone."

Hirta looked down at her hands, calmly folded in her lap. They seemed to belong to someone else. "This is too much to bear," she said.

"It is worse than you know," Rymi said quietly.

"What about the lad? What will you do?"

"All will be made right. First I must find strength again."

"I understand," Hirta said. "He will be safe with us." And then she remembered something, words overheard long ago. "I thought you had an apprentice once. What happened to him?"

~

"Ever get fed up of the cold?" Ross asked, as they sat, side by side, on Tilda's sled. She smiled. "This is not cold. Sometimes it is so cold, Old Ma Frost cannot make any snow."

Ross wondered who Old Ma Frost was. Better not to ask. "How can it get too cold for snow? That's weird."

"It is true. Specks of ice come down instead. Showers of ice seeds, shining and glittering." A wistful look crept into her eyes. "You can hear them, like tiny silver bells. We say it is the stars, whispering secrets to each other."

Ross was restless. He'd been following the astronauts, and he really wanted to see what they were doing. Instead he had to watch smoke rising from Rymi's hut. "What do you think they're saying in there," he said at last.

"You can trust Rymi," Tilda said. "Everyone knows him. He is kind, and wise. He talks to spirits, goes travelling in their worlds."

"Why? He's ancient."

"That is his life. Always, he has helped people."

"And he's worn out. At the end, he was yawning."

"Not yawning, he was breathing in the spirits." Tilda stood up, and began to search among the covers on the sled. "Rymi heals us when we are ill, he finds lost animals, makes amulets. He will help you, I know he will." She pulled out a leather bag. "Lichen," she explained. "They have eaten everything they can reach. Old Olli gets grumpy when he is hungry."

While she fed the reindeer, Ross wandered to the edge of the frozen lake. He was feeling grumpy too. He'd heard more than enough about spooks and spirits and stuff like that. Far away along the horizon stretched a streak of dull red, a forlorn clue to the sun's position. The stars overhead shone cold and bright, while the snowy forest was a hazy deep blue. This was as light as it was going to get.

As Ross turned to go back he saw a fleeting movement in the trees. Maybe it was Rymi's pet. Imagine seeing a real wolf! There'd be no harm in having a look. A narrow track of well-trodden snow led away from the bank, and disappeared among the trees. Stepping carefully so as not to snap any twigs, Ross crept away from the camp, and into the forest.

6

The Deer-star

Ross strained to look among the tangle of trees, unsure of what he might see. Perhaps there'd be a glimpse of a disappearing tail, or the twin lights of wolfish eyes shining between the trunks. He stopped to look back along the track. The air was still, the camp out of sight. No sounds came. Perhaps he'd gone far enough.

Slender birches crowded one side of the track. On the other side stood a tall spruce, stately and aloof, its lower branches reaching almost to the ground. It would be an easy climb. Ross was working out the best route to take, when he noticed something halfway up the trunk. Mottled feathers were perfect camouflage against rough bark, but the grey owl was betrayed by the gleam of its yellow eyes.

"This is unexpected," the owl said. "The Wayfinders were supposed to take you home."

Ross was taken aback. Was this one of Rymi's tricks? "I... I did whistle. The Lights came, just like you said."

"And? What then?"

"I, um, thought about my friend, and her Gran. About talking to them. So that's what I asked for." Did that sound ungrateful? Above the piercing eyes the owl's white eyebrows were bristling.

"That was a mistake. You do not belong here."

Ross felt suddenly cold. "You sound different."

"Hooo-hooo-hoo. Tried not to frighten you. Borrowed a voice you knew." Now it was mocking him, using the white reindeer's voice. Ross glanced along the path, and prepared to run. "I would not do that," the owl said, shuffling along the branch. "Look."

Padding towards them from the direction of the camp came a huge white wolf. It must have been following him all the time.

"Get up here. Quickly," the owl ordered.

Ross hesitated. He wanted to see a wolf, yet now one was here it looked bigger than he'd imagined. He knew he would be safer up the tree. But he wasn't sure about being so close to the owl.

"That is a wolf, stupid. It wants to eat you. Up here, NOW."

Ross ran to the tree, and began to climb. It wasn't as easy as he had thought. The spruce needles caught in his hood, pushing it back so they could prick his face, and when he stretched for the next foothold the long coat kept getting in the way. He was trying to hitch it up when he saw the wolf breaking into a trot.

Suddenly Ross discovered a new skill. He could climb like a squirrel. Snow and debris showered down as he clambered from branch to branch, until he felt high enough to stop. There was no point in going any further. The bird's feathered feet were gripping the branch above with sharp, curved talons. Spitting out some dead spruce needles, Ross reached across to the nearest branch, and heaved himself onto it.

The grey owl was an arm's length away, looking at him with half-closed eyes. "Well, here we are," it said with a low chuckle, "kindred spirits."

The spruce wasn't the most comfortable tree – its springy branches sloped slightly downwards. To feel more secure, Ross swung one leg over so he could settle his back against the trunk. Then, keeping hold of the branch above for balance he leaned over, and looked down. Between the branches he could see the wolf at the foot of the tree, staring up at him. It didn't look as fierce as he'd expected. Thick fur clothed its cheeks, giving its face a chubby appearance, while its ears were pricked forward in a friendly sort of way. It seemed curious, more like a dog than a savage beast. Ross glanced at the owl, wondering if he'd made the right choice.

"We have a problem," the owl said. "Wolves are very patient. It will sit there forever, if it thinks there is a meal at the end of it."

"What can we do?" Ross asked.

"You mean, what can *you* do. I can fly away. Hooo-hooo, hooo-hoo."

Ross hated being laughed at. He leaned back against the trunk and scowled.

"Can't fly, can't take a joke." The owl shook its head in mock disbelief. "Luckily, I have a plan. Watch this."

The grey owl leaned down towards the wolf, spreading its wings wide. Without any warning it gave a low growl, a sound so unexpected that Ross almost fell out of the tree. The wolf responded by curling back its lips to reveal long, cruel fangs.

"See? Easy. Be ready to climb down."

The owl launched itself from the branch, flicking Ross's cheek with the tip of a wing. It circled around silently while the wolf watched. Then with a hideous screech the bird extended its talons, and dropped feet first towards the wolf's head. The animal leapt into the air, jaws snapping viciously, but the owl was too quick. Ross heard a yelp as a claw nicked the wolf's nose. Triumphantly, the grey owl flew a final lap around the spruce, and then disappeared among the trees with the white wolf loping after it.

Ross wasted no time. He felt for a foothold below, and climbed rapidly down through the branches, slithering so easily down the last bit that he wondered if the spruce was glad to be rid of him. Once on the ground he ran back along the track as fast as he could, only slowing down when he was certain he wasn't being followed. Yet as he walked, Ross became convinced the trees were watching him. While passing a group of birches he was sure he could hear whispering, and it wasn't the sound of branches moving, because they weren't. He took deep breaths to steady himself. There were things here that he didn't understand. All the same, they were real. There was no point in trying to ignore that.

Ross was almost himself again when, "Ow!" Something dropped on his head. He scrabbled at his hair, but the object had bounced off. There, half-buried in the snow, sat a cone from a tree. He remembered how he found one before – a really good one – then lost it somehow. Oddly, he had a strange notion that this was the same one. Same size. The same perfect shape. Ross grinned at the idea. This was a forest. There must be millions of them.

As he picked up the cone a trickle of snow came down from the tree above. Ross glanced up, hoping not to see anything, but caught on a snow-laden branch was something resembling a shredded rag. It was a bird, a raven, flexing its black wings while hanging upside-down. The raven tilted its head to return his stare. Then dangling by one foot, it swung backwards and forwards – deliberately showing off,

Ross thought – before letting go of the branch. As it fell, Ross ducked. Yet it was only a shower of snow that hit him. Slow, purposeful wing beats were carrying the raven away, giving a hoarse, throaty laugh as it went.

It seemed highly probable that the raven had dropped the cone. Maybe it even did it on purpose. The last thing Ross needed now was another weird bird, so it was a relief to hear a familiar bark. Fann came bounding towards him with Tilda following. "There you are," she called. "Where have you been?"

"Exploring."

"Exploring? Look at you. What a sight."

Fann jumped up to greet him, and while stroking the dog's head, Ross noticed a rip in the front of his coat. "Felt like climbing a tree."

"I can see. Your head is growing spruce needles. You have a keepsake, too." Ross held up the spruce cone. "This coat has no pockets," he grumbled. Tilda reached out to pat his chest. "There. Inside." As Ross tucked the cone away he decided a diversion was needed, before she had a chance to mention the tear. "I saw the man's wolf," he said proudly. "And the grey owl."

At his mention of the owl, Tilda touched her reindeer amulet. "What did it say?"

"Nothing much. It got rid of the wolf, though."

She looked at him strangely. "Things happen to you," she said. Grudgingly, Ross had to agree. "Suppose so." Stares were exchanged, as each of them tried to make sense of the other. Finally Tilda shrugged. "Rymi is waiting. Next time, say something before you go wandering."

"What for? I'm not scared of wolves."

"There are worse things than wolves," Tilda replied. "Sometimes we see Tatterback here."

~

53

With the fire built up the hut looked quite cosy, except for the animal skull. It was much broader than a human skull, with long, chunky jaws, and pointed canine teeth that gleamed in the firelight. "That is sacred, little stranger," Rymi said. "We do not speak of it." He looked relaxed, with no sign of his previous exhaustion. And despite the imposing appearance of his ritual coat and antlers, he did not seem unfriendly. "Come, sit by the fire," he said. "Tell me your story."

Ross recounted his tale. He was finding that the more often he told it, the more real it became. "And I've seen the owl again, just now in the woods. Your wolf as well."

"You saw Lumi?"

"The grey owl chased him away."

Rymi looked solemn, "Did it speak, this grey owl?" Ross nodded. "It sounded like you, kind of..." Rymi leaned towards him, his copper antlers flickering like flames. "It used my voice to cloud your mind," he said. Ross frowned, protesting that the owl had helped him, but Rymi insisted that he had been deceived. "My wolf meant no harm," he said. "Lumi lured the owl away to keep you safe." Ross's mind was whirling. It was hard to decide what was true, and who was right.

"This grey owl," Hirta asked, "is it someone's soul kin? Who is doing this?"

"We will not name him," Rymi replied, with a wave of his hand. "But know this – he was born under a dark star."

They all stared at Ross, who was scraping the last spruce needles out of his hair. "Listen," Rymi said. "Never go near this person, or his owl. He wishes you nothing but ill." Hirta agreed. "Yes, keep away, whoever he is. Those born under a dark star have a soul dark as a wolf's mouth." Rymi's eyes flicked to his friend, then back to Ross. "No need to fear,

I can protect you. Is there something you carry always? Something special, that has meaning."

Ross thought for a moment. The spruce cone was too new. The other things in his pockets didn't fit the description either. "Suppose there's this," he said reluctantly.

"A scrystone," Rymi murmured. He took the phone in both hands, turning it carefully as though it were an ancient relic. Ross watched anxiously. He hoped it wouldn't come on by accident.

"What is that strange stone?" Tilda asked. "Where is it from?"

"From across the great water," Rymi said. "From a land where ice never melts. It is the frozen blood of a fiery mountain. The black stone is rare, and has great power. This one is finely worked. Was it made especially for you, young stranger?"

"Course not."

"A pity. Something like that holds the best memory. All the same, it is a precious gift. Have you ever used it?"

"Lots," Ross said. This was getting seriously weird. "Games, messaging – sometimes Mum calls. And it takes photos."

"What are... fotos?"

For a moment, Ross was flummoxed. Didn't they know about that either? He looked at the girl, and at her Gran. Their faces were blank. "They're pictures, snaps," he said, riffling through his mind for the right words. "You point it at someone, and their face comes on the screen."

"Ah," Tilda said. "Like when you see your face in a still, dark pool."

"Kind of, yes," Ross said doubtfully. "Except you can keep the face, and look at it whenever you want."

There was a sharp intake of breath, followed by a

horrified silence as the three clutched at their amulets. Rymi was the first to speak. "Do you mean," he asked in a low voice, "you have used the scrystone to catch a person's likeness?"

"Lots of times. I'd show you, but I'm saving the battery."

Rymi was visibly shocked. "This is no game, young stranger. This likeness you make steals a person's vital energy. Their souls are ensnared, as if in a spider's web."

Ross grinned nervously, thinking this might be a joke, but a glance at Tilda's face showed him otherwise. "I didn't know that," he said, quite truthfully.

"Never take the spirits lightly. They will turn on you," Rymi said sternly. "No fotos while you are here."

"I won't. I promise." It was the easiest promise Ross ever had to make.

Rymi closed his eyes, taking some time to compose himself. There was quiet as he concentrated on the scrystone, held between his hands. Then with a fleeting smile he laid it down, and reached for the drum. This time he did not play it, but laid it flat across his knees.

In the centre of the drum-skin was a spiky, abstract design, with drawings of people and animals set around the edge. Rymi placed a triangle of antler on the drum, and tapped the skin sharply several times, causing the triangle to jump about among the images. When he had seen all he needed he took one of the amulets from around his neck, and held it up by its leather thong.

"Look carefully, Ross. What is this?"

"It's, um ... a kind of star."

"A star with eight points. What do you see over there?"

Ross followed Rymi's gaze to one of the curved poles that formed the frame of the hut. Hanging there was a peculiar object. It looked like a much larger version of the amulet, with eight light-brown points arranged in pairs around a central clump of white hair. Ross thought he'd seen something like them before. Suddenly he realised where. "They're hooves," he said. Four reindeer hooves, stuck together."

"The deer-star is my shield against dark forces," Rymi said. "This amulet was carved in its likeness, from the antler of a favourite reindeer. I have worn it these many years, a guard against creeping shadows. Now I give it to you, Ross." Hirta was astounded that he would part with a dedicated amulet. "It is bound to you," she said. "How can you give it away?" Rymi just smiled. "His need is greater."

Ross took the amulet cautiously. It was a perfect miniature of the deer-star on the wall. "Never be without it," Rymi said. "Wear it always, so no harm can come to you."

Tilda said he should put it on, so Ross held the amulet while she tied the thong at the back of his neck. Rymi nodded his satisfaction. "All is well," he declared. "Here, young stranger, take back your scrystone."

"You are letting him keep it?" Hirta exclaimed.

"Why not?" I have seen into his heart."

Hirta stared in disbelief, while Rymi gazed past her to some far distant place. Then suddenly he rubbed his hands together saying, "You must all be hungry."

This signalled the end of the ceremony. Rymi went over to a low platform beside the wall where he laid out his ritual coat, and hung up the drum and headdress. Without the bulky coat he looked very thin. Yet there was an air of determination, of endurance about him, the sum of a lifetime spent in the forest. His hair was long, the colour of wood ash. His clothes were plain – long boots, deerskin breeches, and tunic. Around his neck hung a string of black claws, an animal's tooth, and a disc of antler carved with a reindeer's head. The most striking thing was his wide leather belt studded with carved deer and birds, from which hung a pouch and a knife.

When the white rug had been rolled up and packed away, Tilda went to fetch the gift from their sled. Rymi would never ask for anything, but it was the custom to give something after a ceremony. Hirta had brought berries preserved at leaf fall, and some bread and meat for all of them to share.

The pieces of reindeer meat were speared on sticks, and held over the fire to cook. The others used their knives to cut off bits to eat, but as Ross had no knife Tilda cut some for him. Nothing much was said while everyone enjoyed the meal. When they'd finished Rymi turned to Ross, and asked if he was enjoying his stay with Hirta and Tilda.

"It's alright."

"That is well. You will not mind staying longer."

Ross was a bit surprised, but he nodded silently.

"I owe you a truth," Rymi said. "It was me who brought you here. Or true to say, my soul kin. The white reindeer represents me in other worlds. He does my bidding there. He travels to places where I cannot go, and challenges spirits who wish people harm."

"Was he here before, in your hut?"

"He was."

So, Ross thought, Rymi and the white reindeer were connected in some way. Maybe they were like twins, or two sides of the same person. Or one person in two places at once. "Will he come back? Will I see him again?"

Rymi gave him a slow smile. "All things are possible."

"There's one thing I don't get," Ross said. "How did he find our house? I mean – I wasn't in your spirit world. I was in the real world."

This made Rymi laugh. "You think the place of spirits is an illusion. There are many worlds, young stranger. All are real to those who live in them."

Ross thought hard about this, so hard that his eyebrows knotted together. If everything here was real, that meant some of the things he'd assumed were in his head had actually happened. It was a very disturbing thought. "Why did you pick me?" he asked.

"Well…" Rymi hesitated. "You see, Ross, I was searching for someone else. You were brought here by mistake. For that, I am sorry." Ross forced a smile. He hadn't expected that, and he didn't like it. "Be cheerful," Rymi said. "Few have made such a journey. Come the young moon, I will send you home again."

Ross was confused. Flying with the reindeer had made him feel special, yet it turned out that it was all a mistake. And the news that should have pleased him, that he was going home, brought only disappointment. It was fun, living in a tent. He liked the snow, and the sky crammed with stars. There were things to do here, exciting things. He wasn't ready to go back yet. Hoping it wouldn't come too soon, he tried to remember how many days were left before the new moon.

7

A Grey Stranger

The hearth was a sad sight. White ash filled the ring of stones, so it looked as welcoming as an empty grave. Gloomily they gathered around it, willing the fire to burst into life.

"There," Hirta said. "I see a glow."

Tilda was less hopeful. "We need kindling and bark, to start again," she said, looking at Ross. He groaned. Although he knew that everyone had to pitch in and help, he was tired, and his face was stinging from spruce-needle rash. He didn't feel like doing anything. "Alright," he said grudgingly.

"Leave the door open," Hirta said, "so I can see to clear up." As she took down the cauldron she swung around quickly, forcing Ross to leap across the hearth. "No!" she shouted. "Never do that again."

"What's wrong? What did I do?" Bewildered, Ross looked to Tilda for help. "You crossed the hearth," she said. "That insults the hearth-keeper, even when the ash is cold." Ross burned with indignation. How was he supposed to know? "Hurry," Tilda said. "We need to be quick, before the fire dies completely."

~

Most of the dead wood had already been collected from around the camp, so they went further into the forest. "We only need thin twigs," Tilda said. "Try the lower branches, there might be some fallen twigs caught there. No, not them, the bendy ones are still alive."

Searching for dead twigs wasn't easy in the half-light. Ross was doing his best even though he was weary, with a storm gathering in his head.

Tilda watched him as she peeled the papery birch bark. His attitude was making the task more difficult. Why could he not accept things, as she did? "Nobody likes coming back to a cold hearth. We work together to make it right," she said, pointedly. The lad made no reply, just thrashed about among the branches. Tilda knew she was prodding a wounded bear with a sharp stick, yet she could not stop herself. "Rymi promised to take you home. So why are you not content? The young moon will come soon enough."

He continued to ignore her. Ross was in no mood for chat. He spotted a likely branch on a tree, and reached up to snap it off.

"Ask the tree before doing that," Tilda scolded. "And mind Rymi's amulet. Be careful. Tuck it in."

This was too much. Ross whirled around, rubbing his scalp viciously. "It's not my fault we stayed too long at Rymi's," he shouted. "It's his fault the fire's gone out, and we're messing about in the dark, looking for stupid bits of wood. What's he done for me, anyway? The owl helped with the Lights, and it got rid of the wolf."

Stunned by this outburst Tilda stood still as a stone, a length of peeled bark curling around her hand. "You should listen to Rymi. He gave you the star because you need it. If he says the owl is dangerous, then it is."

There was no reasoning with Ross now. The storm in his head was at full force. "You're just jealous, 'cos the owl taught me how to whistle to the Lights."

"I knew that. Nanna told me, long ago."

"Nanna. Huh! What does she know? She's ancient."

Tilda stared at him, appalled. "What cruel things you say! If that is how you think, go and find your precious owl." Furiously, she gathered up her collection of bark and twigs. "I am going. You can do what you like."

Ross pretended not to hear, just rummaged aimlessly under a bush. Tilda headed off, shouting over her shoulder, "I hope you get eaten by Tatterback." Once she was out of sight Ross stopped pretending. As he straightened up the amulet became caught on a branch, jerking the thong tight. A cascade of snow went down the back of his neck.

"Stupid thing!"

His skin burned where the leather had scraped it. Consumed by rage, Ross wrenched the amulet over his head. He grasped the star in his fist as if to crush it. "Rymi messed up. Why should I listen to him?" he said, addressing the trees. "Anyhow, the owl's more fun."

He was too caught up in his thoughts to notice the dog. Alerted by angry voices, Larna had come to defend Tilda. Now there was no need. She saw the girl set off back to their camp, and was about to follow, when the sound of an object hitting the snow made her prick up her ears. The stranger had thrown something down.

~

Back in the tent, amid the lingering smell of breakfast fish, Hirta prepared to rescue the fire. She kneeled before the hearth, repeating the words she had learned as a child. "Hear me, mothers of my mother. Guide my hands to raise the fire."

If the attempt failed she would have to start from scratch, using the fire-making tools. She didn't hold with using metal and flint. It might upset the hearth-keeper. She'd rather put her trust in Fa's old firebow, even though it took longer. Gently, without disturbing the ash, she lowered the last scrap of bark onto the remaining embers. It was touch and go. But if the hearth-keeper were willing, she wouldn't have the chore of starting again. Why did the lad have to leap across the hearth, just when she needed the firesprite's help?

Hopefully, she stroked the shiny stone. "Hear me, hearth-keeper. Make the flame burn bright for me." She waited. But there was no flame, and no sign of the firesprite.

"Am I too late?" Tilda came rushing in, letting the door slap. She dropped to her knees, allowing the bundle of twigs and bark to tumble from her arms.

Hirta noticed her flushed face. "What ails you?" she asked. "Where is the lad?"

"Oh, he has an awful mood. He said terrible things, so I left him on his own."

"Well, he will have to wait. Pass me some bark."

Hirta took the slither, and held it to the fading glow. At first nothing happened. Then a bright, golden ruffle spread along the edge. They bent over it, blowing very softly, until the ruffle began to flicker and a little flame appeared. "More bark," Hirta said. Soon they were adding twigs, allowing each one to catch before feeding in the next. When the flames were bold enough they added some thicker twigs. At the sight of the fire coming alive again, Hirta began to relax. It was going to be all right.

"Now, tell me what happened."

"It was awful. We were looking for kindling, and he got really angry. Then I said something..." Tilda hung her head. "I said I hoped Tatterback would eat him."

Hirta took a sharp breath. "I hope you didn't speak its real name."

"Of course not, Nanna."

"Good. No need to worry. He will be safe enough."

"I should go and find him."

"No, leave him for a while. Let him cool down. What can happen, anyway? He has Rymi's amulet."

~

Alone in the forest, Ross gazed at the firewood he'd collected. It dawned on him that more could be done with sticks than burning them. He could build a den.

He didn't have to wander far before he found a promising spot. On the edge of a clearing, next to a tree, stood a shrub with arching branches. A gap at the front already looked like a doorway. Ross selected some stout sticks, and pushed them into the snow near the tree trunk, where they formed a short fence angled towards the shrub. He bent some of its branches across, weaving them in and out between the uprights. Then he twisted some twigs off the tree – without asking its permission – and used them to prevent the branches from springing out again.

Ross straightened up to assess his den. It wasn't perfect. But a roof, a wall and a small entrance to crawl through were all the shelter he needed while he waited for the Lights. All that was missing was something dry to sit on, some pine branches like they had in the tent. He turned around to find some, and froze.

At the other side of the clearing stood a figure, leaning on a long walking staff. The last thing Ross had expected, or wanted, was to find someone else here. How long had the man been watching? Ross dodged behind the tree, hoping he hadn't been seen.

"Too late to hide," the stranger called cheerfully.

Ross peered warily at the man from behind his tree. In the twilight everything about him looked grey, like the smoke from damp logs. His round fur hat was grey, and his long fur coat. For a moment Ross thought he was hearing things, that the man was not real, but a shadow.

The stranger strolled into the centre of the clearing. "You made a fine job of that shelter," he said. "Only one thing missing. A fire." He removed one of his mittens, and with a snap of his fingers conjured a blue flame from the tip of his thumb.

Throwing away caution, Ross stepped into the open. "How did you do that?"

The flame flitted, moth-like, from fingertip to fingertip. Then it settled in the man's palm, where it brightened swiftly, flooding his features with light. A smile slipped across the grey man's face. He took a step towards Ross, and used his boot to scrape a hollow in the snow. "Bring your kindling, and lay it down there."

Ross hurried to gather up the remaining wood. With a flick of his hand the stranger threw the blue glow onto the small heap, engulfing it in dazzling flames. In the darkening forest this sudden burst of light was mesmerising.

"A happy chance, that we should meet,' the man said, in a voice smooth as moonlight on water.

Ross looked at him carefully. He was younger than Rymi, with wide cheekbones, a stubbly jaw, and skin so pale it was grey too. He didn't look threatening, not at all. But he did remind Ross of something.

"Are you, um," Ross began. "Have I seen you before?"

"You might have," the stranger said.

"There was this huge grey owl…" Ross hardly believed what he was about to say next. "Was that you?"

"A quick mind. I like that."

"Hey, you're the owl! What's it like?"

The man leaned on the staff, and smiled. "Well, flying is the best bit. But hunting voles is almost as good. I can hear the little sounds they make, running along their tunnels under the snow. I sit very still, and listen. I can hear them in their little world, but they never know I'm there – until I pounce, and break through the snow to snatch them up."

"Sounds amazing."

"Then I eat them. Swallow them, headfirst. Fur, tail, and everything."

"Eurgh. That's horrible."

"Not for an owl."

Ross grinned. "What's your name?" The grey man seemed surprised by that question. "I used to have one, once. No longer." Ross tried to imagine not being Ross, but it made his brain hurt. After all, everyone has a name. Even goldfish. "That's really weird."

"It suits me," the man said.

A faint haze hung between them, from the blue flames that flickered among the wood. Standing in the forest in the frosty air, with stars trembling above, Ross felt as though he was in a dream. "I was, kind of, hoping I'd see you," he admitted.

"Were you now," said the man who was sometimes an owl. "Does Rymi know that?"

"Not exactly." Ross felt the sting of guilt. "Do you know him?"

"Everyone knows Rymi," the grey man replied, with an accomplice's smile.

8

Flames That Chill

The tent felt like home again, with a full kettle singing over a cheery fire. At last the herders could take off their coats and relax.

Hirta was in a thoughtful mood. "The years rush to meet me," she said. "One day this tent will be yours. You should be doing the greeting, so the hearth-keeper accepts you."

Tilda had not expected that. The greeting was something Nanna had always done.

"You have enough years," Hirta said. "And you have the words by heart."

That was true – there were no secrets when you shared a tent. Tilda had heard her elder-Ma countless times, soothing the sprite with flattering words. "If you think it would not mind."

Tilda knelt by the shiny hearthstone. Her hand shook a little as she passed it over the smooth surface. She took a deep breath. "Keeper of the hearth, be with us. Keep away the cold and darkness, keep away the ache of hunger, keep away all harm this day." For a moment everything was still. Then one of the logs fell apart with a splutter, spilling out a shower of bronze beads.

"Go on," Hirta whispered.

"Keeper of the hearth, be welcome," Tilda said, dipping her head slightly like Nanna always did.

"Now say we are sorry for the lad."

Tilda thought for a moment, while the beads arranged themselves into the shape of a cloudberry. The berry tried several metallic sheens before settling on gold. "We are sorry, firesprite, for crossing your hearth. We meant no offence."

"None taken. All forgotten," the sprite said, snapping into its goblin form. It must have been pleased with the cloudberry because it kept it in place of its usual head. The berry smirked. "Good to see a young face for a change."

Hirta grimaced. She had never liked the firesprite's sly wit. All the same, she was glad it had accepted Tilda. The hearth-keeper was in good spirits – it leapt to the topmost log where its body began to spin, faster and faster, until there was only a grinning wisp of smoke. Then it vanished altogether.

Hirta breathed a sigh of relief. "You did well. It likes you."

"Do you think so? Really?"

"Just remember, it is not always friendly. Fire spirits can be very ill tempered. But you must treat it with respect, whatever its mood. No shouting. No storming off." They both laughed. But soon Tilda looked troubled. "Ross is a stranger, it was wrong to leave him."

Hirta sighed. "Have some tea first. Then go and fetch him." She was reaching for the kettle when they heard a bark. "There's Larna," she said.

As soon as Tilda opened the door, the dog rushed in with something dangling from her mouth. Larna dropped her find among the pine branches on the floor, and stepped backwards, wagging her tail. She watched intently as Tilda bent down to pick it up.

"It's the star! Oh, Nanna, he lost the star."

~

The grey man was rearranging the sticks in the fire, using a long branch as a poker. "You like a good story?" he asked. Ross said he did. "Then I'll tell you an old tale. Sit for a while, there, on that tree stump."

Ross looked around, certain that he'd not seen a tree stump while he was making his den. Yet there it was, covered in snow. How had he missed it? With a shrug, Ross brushed off the snow, and sat down.

On the other side of the fire his companion stretched out, leaning on one elbow in the snow. The man seemed not to care about the cold. Ross wished that he, too, had a coat that kept him warm. Since he'd stopped moving about he could feel a chill through the rip in the front. Pulling the deer-hair close, he leaned towards the fire hoping for warmth. But he felt no heat. Blue flames danced among the wood, yet none of it was burning. Every twig looked the same as when he found it.

Ross opened his mouth to say something, but at the same moment the man began to speak. "This is a true story, about someone who talked to spirits," he said. "Someone like you. A bit older, perhaps. He started by talking to the Wayfinders. Every night he left the warmth of his tent, hoping to see their torches in the sky. Soon they became his friends. He had no more need of his kin. He left his family, and became a wanderer." The man paused to glance at Ross, weighing the effect of his words.

"One day, while he was hunting birds in the forest, the wanderer came across the tent of a healer. This healer made visits to the spirit world, where he gained the knowledge to do good deeds. Eventually the young wanderer became his apprentice. Those were good days. There were families in the forest then..."

Here the storyteller seemed to lose the thread of his tale. For a long time he stared into the fire, apparently struggling with his thoughts. Then abruptly he sat up, and resumed the story.

"Like you, the wanderer was quick to learn. He mastered the trance. He discovered the secrets of the sacred drum. He found his soul kin, his animal self. Best of all was the day he earned his special coat. That was a great adventure. The apprentice went alone into another world, for the first time." The man's eyes narrowed. "What do you think he found there?"

"I don't know."

"Fire-demons! Rushing from every side, like red-hot sparks in a gale. He fought them off, yet more came, burning him with their fiery arrows. It was a fierce fight. One – the boldest – came at him with a blazing spear. He dodged, feeling it slice into his side. The spear went right through! It lodged there, burning, sticking out before and behind."

Ross sat motionless, his eyes wide. "What did he do?"

"The only thing he could do. He grasped the spear, and ripped it out."

"I bet that really hurt."

The man's mouth twisted into a wry smile. "Every apprentice must be tested. Pushed to his limit. Only then is he worthy."

"What happened next?"

"He threw the spear with all his strength, catching the fire-demon full in the chest. The demon exploded in a cloud of splinters. The wanderer had practised his skills well. He was wounded severely, yet none of them escaped."

"Wow. Did he go back?"

"Many times. On one journey he discovered a great truth. A truth about the Wayfinders." The man paused, pressing his fingers to his forehead. He seemed to have a headache coming on. His eyes closed, and after a few seconds opened again, slowly.

"Tell me," Ross said impatiently, "about the Wayfinders."

"You know what they can do. Raw power, that's what they are. Good or ill means nothing to them."

Something was happening to the man's eyes. It wasn't easy to judge colour in the twilight, but if they'd been yellow before, Ross was sure he would have noticed.

"Those who know the Wayfinders can channel their energy. As you did, when you called them down," the man said, growing animated. "Together we can be strong, more powerful than that old fool Rymi. What do you say?"

Ross felt chilled to his bones. Those eyes weren't human. They were owl's eyes, round and yellow with hard black pupils. That voice was the owl's voice. Rows of feathers were edging the man's jaw, right up to his grey fur hat. Only that wasn't fur any longer.

"Thanks," Ross mumbled, "but I don't think I'll bother."

"Think of it." The grey man was on his feet now. "All that power, doing our bidding."

Ross shook his head. He'd made a terrible mistake. And he didn't want to hang around while the man turned into a bird. He tried to stand up, but something was wrong. His feet wouldn't move. He couldn't even feel them. He looked at the dark boots, now white with frost, and bent down to brush it off. The soft deerskin was solid. His feet were numb, encased in ice. On a rising tide of panic, Ross snatched at the neck of his coat. The star wasn't there. It wasn't there.

The man shrugged. "Your choice," he said, indifferently. "Now meet your new friends."

He swept up his hands. Long feathers, growing where his fingers had been, whipped the fire into a blue inferno. Above the cold flames a column of mist was forming. Vague shapes struggled within it like animals in a trap. Ross was filled with dread. Was he meant to join them? Those shades could have been human, once. Hands stretched out from the mist as they drifted up into the darkness. Mouths opened in silent despair, pleading for help that would never come.

It was agony to watch, but Ross had no choice. If only he could run! Still the ice clasped him fast. He squeezed his eyelids shut yet the nightmare remained. When he looked again he saw the man through the mist, grinning at the captives with outstretched wings.

Ross yelped. Something had hold of his arm.

"Hush. It's me." Tilda was crouching behind him, pushing the amulet inside his mitten. When the star touched his palm a flickering, like flames, spread quickly up his arm. Then the flames were in his feet, and they hurt like anything. "Hurry," Tilda whispered, "before he–"

As she spoke, the mist vanished. The blue flames died. The man's face was a storm cloud. "Who is that?" he growled.

Ross, fighting his thawing feet, stumbled over the tree stump. Tilda pulled him over, and they fell into the den, scattering sticks everywhere. On hands and knees they scrambled through the tangle, tumbling out on the other side covered in twigs and snow. Tilda sprang up, pulling Ross to his feet. Before they could take a step, a shadow swept in front of them, blotting out the trees.

"Is that *him*?"

Ross nodded silently. When he'd seen the grey owl before it had looked like a real bird. Now there was no such pretence. Yet neither was this apparition human. Its true form, whatever that may have been, was masked by dappled feathers. Enormous grey wings stretched wide, dashing all hope of escape.

"Owl eyes," Tilda gasped.

They were helpless as the terrifying vision loomed over them, wingtips reaching out like charred fingers. Sour air caught in their throats, making them cough. Somewhere nearby Larna began to bark. One glance from their tormentor was enough to reduce her to a whimper.

"You next," the shape-shifter said, focusing his attention on Tilda.

"Leave her alone," Ross shouted. He limped forward to stand between them, Rymi's amulet held firmly in his hand.

"So brave, now you have your lucky charm." The monster gave the amulet a scornful glance, although he didn't come any closer. "Drop it, so we can be friends again."

You wish, Ross thought, slipping the amulet around his neck.

"Pathetic little vole, creeping to your master." The massive wings beat with menacing slowness, stirring the powdery snow. The yellow eyes slid back to Tilda.

Ross blinked in the draught. "We're not scared of you. We're going now."

The shape-shifter smiled, a crafty, malicious smile. "Does she agree? Perhaps you should ask her."

Ross turned to Tilda. Her eyes were blank, her face without expression. He seized her arm, shouting, "Stop it. Don't look at him!" He tried to shake her. She was rigid, as unyielding as a fencepost.

"She has no need for you," the monstrous owl said. "She has new friends now."

Please, no, Ross thought. Not the ghosts in the mist. Panicking, he pulled Tilda roughly by the wrist, but still she didn't move. "What've you done?"

"A trick. A spell. One of my best."

"What?" Ross shouted. "You can't. You've got to undo it."

"Careful, Voleheart." The yellow eyes narrowed. "She loves the forest, doesn't she? Loves the trees? Well now she is a tree. I do like a happy ending."

Ross was desperate. He had to save Tilda, but how? The owl was dissolving into a confusion of greys. The feathered robe was shrinking to the shape and size of a real bird. It was smaller, much smaller. If I'm going to do something, he thought, this is my chance.

Ross launched himself at the flurry of grey feathers, throwing his arms around the newly formed body. Somehow he managed to pin down one wing. When the star touched the feathers the smell of singeing almost choked him, yet Ross was determined not to give up. But this owl had a man's strength. It twisted around, striking Ross across one eye with the edge of its other wing. Ross let go. Both wings opened out. The owl started to rise. Ross made a grab for the tail, and held on. The owl lurched clumsily to left and right, trying to throw him off. In the brief struggle Ross was lifted off the ground. Then, with a ghastly screech, the grey owl wrenched itself free.

Ross fell on his back in the snow, a long, striped feather clutched in one hand. The owl flew higher as if heading for the trees. Then wheeling around, he hurtled back shrieking, "Thief! Thief!"

Instinctively Ross rolled aside. His face pressed into the snow as cruel talons scythed past his head. He wasn't a helpless vole. The owl could do nothing, so long as he wore the amulet. Ross raised his head to watch the grey shadow melt into the forest.

As soon as the owl had gone Ross got to his feet, and examined his prize. The strong, banded tail feather was much longer than his hand. But however impressive, it was only a feather, after all. Why did the owl want it back? His first impulse was to throw it away. Then he saw Tilda, motionless as a statue. Larna was creeping towards her with head held low, feebly wagging her tail. The dog's nose touched Tilda's hand. No words of greeting came in return.

Tilda didn't deserve this. She had been really brave. Ross vowed that the owl wouldn't get away with it. He looked again at the feather, and knew he should keep it. At that moment Larna sat down in the snow, pointed her muzzle at the stars, and howled as though her heart were breaking.

9

A Lost Soul

Hirta was snoozing by the fire. She had not intended to. But it felt so good to be back in her tent, with the fire burning merrily, that sleep had been irresistible. With Fann snuggling in beside her she drifted into the world of dreams, where she was always young.

A remarkable thing happened. One of her cows gave birth to a beautiful calf, so wonderful that all Hirta's relatives came to see. As the young animal grew the family was blessed with good fortune. But Hirta felt uneasy. She knew the reindeer's destiny lay beyond the everyday. And as she feared, one morning the beautiful deer could not be found.

Hirta became restless. She had to find the young reindeer. Her body felt too big, and much too heavy. From far away a voice was calling, "Wake up, Nanna. Stir yourself." She opened her eyes, to find herself in the tent. The fire burned fiercely, and beside it stood a young hunter clothed in golden furs. He held Tilda's bow with an arrow notched, ready to fire. Hirta wondered at the vision. It looked so real.

"Stir yourself," the voice insisted. "A shadow moves against your kin."

Hirta woke up with a start. The hunter was still there. Fear gripped her – she had never seen the firesprite in that guise before. "What do you mean? What shadow?"

"A great bird hovers over her soul."

"Her? Oh, no. Where's Tilda?"

"Do not delay," the firesprite said. "The hearth is safe in my keeping."

In a daze Hirta pulled on her coat and mittens. Seizing Old Olli's harness, she rushed outside with Fann bounding beside her. All was quiet. No sign of Tilda, or her sled. Where was she? Where to look?

As Hirta cast around to find the freshest tracks, she heard a sound that chilled her heart. The howling of a dog tore through the silence. It was Larna, singing her misery to the forest.

~

Ross leaned on a tree to get his breath. He had found Miri tethered by the track, but the deer was so jumpy he hesitated to approach him. Tilda lay nearby, unmoving. She couldn't walk, so he'd had to drag her this far. It was difficult walking backwards, dragging the unconscious girl, while Larna nipped at his heels all the way. The dog seemed to think all this was his fault.

Once more Ross placed his hands under Tilda's arms, and started to pull her through the snow. Larna began to circle them again, eyeing him warily. Then something else caught the dog's attention. Ross heard the swish of an approaching sled. Don't let it be the owl, he thought. But it was only Old Olli bringing Tilda's grandmother.

Hirta leapt from her sled and rushed over. "What happened?" she demanded, her face hard with fear.

"I was trying to get her on the sled," Ross said, in a faint voice.

"I mean before that," Hirta snapped. She fell on her knees in the snow, trying to cradle Tilda in her arms. But the girl's body was too stiff and awkward. Hirta could only bend over her, crooning helplessly, "Oh, little calf. Oh, my heart's treasure."

Ross fidgeted with embarrassment. He'd never seen such raw grief before, and didn't know what to say. He felt guilty too, as he realised the seriousness of Tilda's plight, and remembered his part in bringing it about. "The grey owl was here," he said, in a small voice. "It was really scary. Tilda gave me the star, and we tried to run away, but the owl caught us. It was staring at Tilda. She went all funny…" He stopped, sensing the woman's growing anger.

"You better not be involved with that monster," Hirta growled. "Tell me you are not."

"No, honest! He wanted to kill me!" Ross saw her expression. He didn't dare to tell the whole truth.

"Or was it you? You did this. With your Ma's scrystone."

"No, no! It was the owl!" Ross cupped a hand over his throbbing eye. "I tried to stop him," he added, weakly.

For a moment Hirta glared at the star amulet, now hanging safely around his neck. Then she said, "We need to get her home. Don't just stand there. Lift her feet. Carefully, now." They laid Tilda on Hirta's sled, tucking hides under her arms to prevent her from rolling off. Ross set off, leading Old Olli, while Hirta followed with the skittish reindeer, never taking her eyes off Tilda.

While they were carrying her into the tent Tilda began to tremble. "Are you hurting, little calf?" Hirta asked anxiously, as they put her down on the bed. "Maybe she's scared of the fire," Ross said. "She thinks she's a tree, and trees get burned by fire, don't they?"

Hirta bent over to kiss her, but Tilda's half-open eyes showed no spark of recognition. Her arms were unbending, held out from her sides like drooping branches. "What was that about trees? Tell me what happened," Hirta demanded. "Every detail."

Reluctantly, Ross told her about meeting the stranger. "Oh, you wretch," she said. "We warned you not to talk to him. Why stay, when you knew who he was?" There was nothing Ross could say to this, except that he was sorry.

"Sorry!" Hirta put her head in her hands. "What use is that? He willed a terror on her. My lovely girl! What if she is beyond help? What do I say to her poor Ma, who trusted me?"

Hoping to make her feel better, Ross rummaged inside his coat, and brought out the owl's feather. It had got a bit bent from being in the same pocket as the spruce cone. "I managed to get this," he said. "Perhaps it'll help."

"Where did you get that?" Hirta gasped, clutching at the bear's tooth hidden under her shawl. She couldn't have looked more horrified if the shape-shifter had materialised in front of her.

"It's the owl's. From its tail."

"Old Ones, save us," she shouted. "Get that thing out of here. Outside. Now! And stay there."

Ross didn't want to be out in the freezing air. He was empty and lonely, and his feet hurt. His eye was sore where the owl's wing had struck him. Everything was going wrong, and all of it was his fault. He wandered over to where the reindeer were standing, waiting to be unharnessed from the sleds. They lifted their heads as he approached.

"Hello, Miri," he said sadly, raising his hand to stroke the animal's neck as he'd done once before. But the reindeer suddenly swung his head sideways, butting Ross hard with his single antler, and sending him sprawling. Ross lay in the snow like a fallen star. "I'm sorry, Miri." The words tumbled out. "I didn't mean it to happen." The reindeer shook his head, and stepped closer. Ross didn't care if Miri meant to trample him. He deserved it. Lacking the will to move, he simply closed his eyes. But all he felt was gentle breath, and the softness of Miri's nose as the reindeer sniffed his face.

"A touching scene," said a man's voice. "We will make a herder of you yet."

Ross sat up quickly. Why was he here, so soon after they'd left his camp? Rymi rose from his sled to stand beside his reindeer, affectionately scratching its neck. In his brown deer-hair coat, fur hat, and dark leggings, he looked uncannily like a reindeer himself. Ross wanted to say to him, please help Tilda, but he was overwhelmed by shame. He got to his feet in silence.

"What are you doing out here, young stranger?"

"Hirta threw me out."

"Why would she do that?"

Ross thought hard. He mustn't tell Rymi what he'd done with the star. "Tilda isn't well. It was the grey owl. I pulled a feather from its tail, and when I showed it to Hirta she got really angry."

"I should think I did, "Hirta said, throwing back the tent door. "You are balm for a troubled soul, Rymi. No-one could be more welcome." He lifted a large bundle from his sled. It chinked softly as he shifted it under one arm. "I saw your need. How is Tilda?"

"Between sleep and waking," Hirta said, standing aside so he could enter the tent. "She does not move, she does not speak." Rymi paused at the door to glance over at Ross, saying, "He should come in."

"Not with that disgusting feather."

Rymi nodded. "Go inside. I will not be long."

He waited until the door closed. Then he put down the bundle, saying in a low voice, "She is right about that feather. It could draw the owl to us. We need to hide it from his sight." From inside his coat he produced a length of fine leather, soft and delicate as a piece of silk, with symbols on it like the ones on his drum. "Hare's skin," Rymi explained. "Powerful against hidden forces." He draped the leather over his outstretched hand, telling Ross to place the feather in the centre. At the sight of it Rymi screwed up his eyes, as though it pained him even to look at it. He certainly took care not to touch the feather himself, folding the leather precisely so no stray wisp was showing. "Quickly," he said, "tell me what happened with Tilda."

"We were running away. He was kind of half owl, and he flew after us. I tried to save her," Ross said earnestly, "but he was staring at her, and her eyes went all strange, and she couldn't move. Then he changed into a proper owl. I grabbed his tail, but he got away. I ended up with the feather."

"That took courage," Rymi said, watching him closely.

"Will it help?" Ross asked. His carefully edited report had, it seemed, been accepted.

"Everything has a part to play." Rymi tucked the wrapped feather inside his coat. Then he asked casually, "How did Tilda chance to meet him?"

This was it. Ross couldn't lie, not when those steady, grey eyes were fixed on his. It was like looking at a wintry ocean, while across the water an unknown fate was speeding towards him. "She came to help me," he said miserably. "She brought the star."

The words were barely spoken when a towering wave came crashing through his mind, flinging aside thoughts like so many pebbles. Memories were ransacked, his secret guilt revealed. Ross was sinking, drowning. Then abruptly the force fell back, leaving him stranded. "I got mad. Threw it away," he managed to say.

"I saw that."

"It was stupid. I'm really sorry." Shocked and bewildered, Ross struggled to gather his scattered thoughts. Everything was jumbled up, and in the wrong place. He couldn't doubt Rymi's power now. Afraid of catching that terrible gaze once more, Ross lowered his head to wait for the angry words. Instead, he felt a hand on his shoulder. "Never again will I take your thoughts," Rymi said. "I had to see the truth, though. That one has beguiled many. You are not the first."

Now the worst was out, the rest was easier to tell. "He made a fire that wasn't hot," Ross said, "with blue flames. It was so cold my feet were frozen. I couldn't move. The smoke was like mist with ghosts in it."

"Those were stolen souls," Rymi said quietly. "Now you know the value of my amulet."

"Is that what he did to Tilda?" Ross whispered, feeling he could risk a look. He saw no anger in the man's face, only sadness. "Let us hope not," Rymi said.

~

Although not unexpected, the scene inside the tent was upsetting. Tilda lay perfectly still under the reindeer hides, her plaited hair draped over one shoulder. Ross couldn't tell if she was breathing. On one side sat Hirta, clasping her hands together so fiercely that the knuckles were white. Stretched out limply at Tilda's feet was Larna, her body an image of dejection.

Rymi knelt down beside Hirta. He placed a hand on Tilda's forehead. For a while everything was silent – even the logs on the fire stopped crackling. It seemed as though an age had passed before he gave his verdict.

"One of her souls is missing."

Hirta's face crumpled, and a tear spilled over. "Can you save her? Will she be herself again?"

"Take heart," Rymi said softly. "This is not strange to me."

Hirta dabbed at her eye with the edge of her shawl. Then suddenly she turned on Ross who was standing near the door, trying his best to be invisible. "We took him in, cared for him, and this is our reward. She would never have been out there, if he had not lost your amulet."

Rymi took her hand. "Be strong, for Tilda. We will bring her back. As for him," he added, looking directly at Ross, " he was foolish to lose my amulet, but he is wiser now."

Ross felt his heart leap. Rymi knew he'd thrown away the star, yet he wasn't going to tell. It was true what Tilda had said, about him helping people. Rymi was giving him another chance. "Don't know what it means," Ross mumbled, " but the owl said she was a tree."

"Then there is hope," Rymi replied. "Tree spirits seldom do harm."

Ross dared to ask if he could help, and Rymi nodded. "You can help me with the reindeer."

It felt good to be outside, doing something practical. Miri and Olli seemed happy to see them – no doubt they were eager to be freed from the sleds. Rymi removed their harnesses, while Ross collected them up. When they came to his reindeer, Rymi unhitched him from the sled but left his harness on. The deer stood calmly as he knotted the traces loosely across his back. "Eat well, friend," he said fondly, as he led the reindeer among the trees. "Soon I will have a task for you."

"What about your camp?" Ross asked, struggling with the tangle of straps and collars. "What if the owl goes there while you're away?" Rymi knotted the rein around a branch, and stroked his reindeer's back. "The spirits keep it defended. As for visitors from this world, my wolf is enough to discourage them."

"What do you think the owl's doing now?"

"Nothing," Rymi said. "Shifting form drains energy. While he rests, we have a chance."

When they went back inside they found Hirta more composed, and the guardian gleaming with a fresh coating of fat. Hirta had made a brew, and each cradled a bowl as they sat around the hearth. Her offer to fry some meat had been refused – Rymi said no, he never ate before a trance. Hirta told him she didn't feel like eating anyway, with Tilda lying there like that. Ross could have managed something, quite a lot of something, but it didn't seem the right time to say so. Tentatively, he touched his bruised eye. Already it was a bit puffy.

"I have something for that," Rymi said. He reached inside the mysterious bundle, and brought out a small oval container. "This balm will speed the healing. Smooth it around your eye. Use it as often as you like."

"Thanks."

The little pot had been made from a section of antler. Its snug-fitting lid came off with a whisper, releasing a fresh, ferny smell. Ross dipped a finger into the green ointment, and smeared it over the bruise.

"Now we begin," Rymi said. "Returning a soul is perilous. Everything must be right. This tent must be purified, and all of us within it."

Hirta frowned. "What about herbs? We may not have enough."

Rymi rummaged in the bundle again, this time finding a pouch of juniper. "This should be enough. While you do that, I will put up my tent. Then the spirits will find Tilda."

Ross asked what he could do. "There is one thing," Rymi said, looking at him thoughtfully. "All will go better if the owl does not interfere. We need someone to distract him."

This required some thought. Ross knew all too well what the owl was capable of, because his feet kept reminding him. They felt as though some nasty little demon was tickling them with a lighted candle. He flexed his toes, and rubbed his boots together, trying to banish the awful sensation. It was not a success. But really he had no choice. He owed it to Tilda. And this time he'd have the star. That changed everything. "I'll do it," he said.

Rymi smiled. "I never doubted you."

"Um, what will I have to do?"

"You have seen a bird lure a fox away from her nest?" Ross had not. He shook his head. "The bird hobbles away, dragging one wing as if it is broken. She looks pitiful, helpless, an easy target. Predators like an easy kill. So the fox gives up its search for the nestlings, and follows the injured bird."

Ross scratched his head. He didn't understand, but Hirta did. "Is it safe? Look what happened to Tilda. Do we want the lad harmed as well?"

"The bird always escapes," Rymi said. "When the fox pounces, she flies away."

Hirta was not reassured. She looked anxiously at Tilda, so pale and so still. Ross wasn't worried about himself – the only thing that registered with him was the bit about flying away. "I'll be alright," he said cheerfully. Rymi pointed out that his amulet gave Ross protection. "And he can take my sled, with the swiftest of all reindeer."

85

For once Hirta was too exhausted to argue. She told Ross he was a very brave lad. He gave her a wild grin. Already he was imagining the sled racing through the forest.

Rymi got up from the fire, and stooped to open the door. "Hirta," he said, "would you look at his feet? We need our bird to be fit."

10

The Decoy

"This is no easy thing," Rymi said, as he checked the deer's harness to make sure all was secure. "You could still change your mind."

"It's alright," Ross replied. "I'm ready."

No adventurer could have been better prepared or, it was fair to say, more pampered. Hirta had bathed his frost-nipped feet, and rubbed them with deer fat and herbs. She had replaced the old sedge lining in his boots, and given him soft, calfskin socks so that his feet glowed with warmth. She gave him a fur cap to wear under his hood, and a half-moon bag containing strips of dried meat, "Because cold makes you hungry. Make sure you eat."

She had even lent him Tilda's knife in case of an emergency. Finally, a few hasty stitches closed the rip in his coat, and he was ready to go. As he strode over to the sled Ross felt ready for anything.

Now he was more accustomed to reindeer, Ross could see that this one was special. Tall and muscular, he looked as though he could run forever. He was handsome, too. On his forehead was a white star, and the dark hair on his sides was tipped with white, making his coat look frosted.

"Sula is his name," Rymi said. "You like him, I can see."

"Hello, Sula." As Ross spoke, the reindeer turned his head to look at him. Startled by the animal's intelligent expression Ross felt compelled to add, "Me and you have a really important mission."

"Come, settle yourself on the sled," Rymi said. "Now take the reins. No, like this. If you pull too hard, he will stop. Hold them gently, so he can just feel it. If you want to go faster, let the reins go loose."

"Where are we going?"

"Sula will know."

By now it was deep night, with brilliant stars crowding the sky. Rymi, wearing his white healer's coat, leaned over to whisper in the reindeer's ear. As he straightened up the amulets on his back shifted, clinking and gleaming. "Sula will not fail you," he said. "He is sure-footed, brave, and strong. Play your part, and all will be well."

"How do you know where Tilda is?" Ross asked.

"Trees see everything. They whisper it to the air. My bird-spirits hear, and they sing it to me. Her missing soul is in a stand of young birch."

"That's weird. She must be scared."

"Tilda is safe, for now. Anything else?"

Ross thought for a moment. "What if the owl doesn't come?"

"He will come," Rymi said. "He has no choice. The feather is part of him. He knows I could use it against him."

This was a surprise. Ross put his hand into the deerskin bag, feeling for the slim parcel with the feather inside. "Why don't you do that, then? Make him let Tilda go."

"Can we trust him? Cruel tricks are his life's work."

Ross frowned. "Why's he like that?"

"It is his nature," Rymi answered, with the faintest hint

of impatience. "All are born children of the Sun. But some of us grow attracted to decay."

"He can be alright sometimes."

"Pity is wasted on him," Rymi said sharply. "He chose the path he treads. Never forget what he did to Tilda. Remember those lost souls."

"I know. I won't forget."

"Enough talk," Rymi said, clapping Ross on the back. He stepped away from the sled, and called to the reindeer. Sula set off at once. Ross had just enough time to see Rymi raise his hand in farewell.

Sula was heading away from the lake, and soon they reached the spot where Ross had met the grey man. His stomach tightened as he glimpsed the clearing through the trees. Then it was behind them, and they were rushing further along the starlit track. As they passed between some groups of birch Ross thought of Tilda. He hoped she wasn't too scared. At least Rymi would be on the way to rescue her, while he was heading into danger with only a reindeer to help him. It was the weirdest feeling.

~

Rymi looked up as Hirta entered his tent. "How does she fare?" he asked.

"The same."

How bare it is in here, Hirta thought, as she closed the tent door. Just a few branches covered with reindeer hides.

She knelt down opposite him. Rymi picked up the drum, and tapped the skin softly, all the while gazing steadily into the fire. The logs burned quietly, their blackened bark threaded with gold.

Rymi's song began in a whisper, rising to a murmur for the words of incantation. Some phrases he repeated, and here Hirta joined her voice to his. Only when all the spirits were present did their voices fall silent. The rhythm of the drum had become a heartbeat – slow, slower, and then scarcely audible. Feeling herself drawn into the trance, Hirta pressed her nails down hard into her palms. She had to keep awake to watch over Tilda.

Finally the drumbeat ceased, and the drum slipped from Rymi's hands. His voyaging soul was pulled into the realm of spirits. His other self that belonged to this world slumped to one side, and lay as if sleeping. Hirta crept out, and hurried back to her own tent.

~

After a while the track began to rise up the side of a hill. Sula slowed to a walk as the way became steeper while Ross leaned forward, trying to keep the sled straight by using his feet as he'd seen Tilda do. In the starlight all was smoothed out, so that everything looked oddly flat. It was less eerie on the other side where the ground sloped away, and friendly stars glittered between the branches.

Eventually they reached a clearing below the top of the hill. Here the reindeer stopped. Silhouetted against the snow were some old stones – this must be the place Rymi had told him about. Ross jumped off the sled to have a closer look.

There were three stones, resting one on top of another. On the bottom was an irregular rock with smoothed-off edges. The middle stone was smaller, shaped like an egg, and the largest one on top was triangular. The lichens growing on them showed that they had been there for a very long time. Ross wondered what they were for. Rymi had said very little, only that this was a special place.

Ross turned to look through the gap between the trees. Below the hill snow-bound land stretched on and on, endlessly blue beneath the net of stars. The sky was so dark

90

and still compared to home – no satellites, no winking aircraft, and no light pollution from a town over the horizon. Ross shivered at its eeriness. This was like seeing into the past. But the feeling was soon dispelled when a white veil appeared. "Look, Sula," he said excitedly, as the Lights flowed up the sky. For a moment he was tempted to whistle to them again, until he remembered their power, and felt afraid. While he hesitated the aurora froze, then slowly faded away.

Ross knew he couldn't put it off any longer. He reached inside the half-moon bag, slung safely across his body, to bring out the hare-skin parcel. Cautiously, he began to unwrap it. According to Rymi, the owl would know when the feather was revealed. He would be drawn to it. Would that take long? Ross sat down awkwardly in the snow, trying to look as though he'd had an accident. Not too far from the sled. He had to be ready to jump back on.

While Sula nibbled at the lichen on the stones Ross waited, his stomach churning. Would it be the man in grey, or the owl? He might come as something else, something really terrifying. Whatever it was, it could happen at any moment. After reassuring himself that the star was still around his neck, Ross improved his pose by twisting one leg sideways so it looked more dramatic. He waited a bit longer. Nothing happened.

Feeling disappointed, even a bit bored, he jabbed the feather into the snow. He envied the phone, tucked safely in his bed along with the spruce cone. Then he remembered he was wearing Tilda's knife belt.

Ross hooked a thumb over the belt. His fingers traced the criss-cross pattern on the sheath then closed around the handle. He drew the knife slowly, feeling the weight of it in his hand. He touched the point of the blade with one finger. It was sharp, all right. It seemed a pity not to try it.

Turning to the sled he selected a place at the front, on one of the curved-up runners. With great care he scratched an upright line into the wood. Next he tried a curve, but that went a bit wrong. He finished off with another straight line. Satisfied with his angular "R", he slid the knife back into its sheath.

Still nothing was happening. Ross wondered if Rymi was on the soul journey yet. He'd no idea how long it had been since he set out with Sula. Without the phone he had no sense of time. It didn't matter much though. Time was different here. People just did things when they needed doing.

Ross scowled. This was hopeless. It was taking far too long.

Then he had a brilliant idea. When he'd caught hold of the owl, the star had singed its feathers. It might speed things up if he did that now. With the amulet in one hand, he brushed the owl's feather across it. The edges writhed. He tried pressing the end of it onto the star. The end sizzled. A little curl of smoke rose up, and as Ross watched it, he forgot why he was there.

An angry shriek reminded him. It sounded much closer than he would have liked.

"You dare to do that, here, of all places." The owl looked angry. Its feathers were sticking out at odd angles, like his mother's breakfast hair. Quickly, Ross pushed the feather into the bag, and scrambled onto the sled. Sula was already moving as he grabbed the reins.

"You called me from my rest. You'll regret that, thief."

The owl's threat faded into the distance as they skimmed along the track. But before long Ross saw the grey bird keeping pace with them, appearing and disappearing between the trees. He grinned. The plan was working.

As the sled creaked, and the runners hissed, Ross was gripped by a wild joy. He was being hunted, but he didn't care. He was feeling the thrill of outrunning the hunter. Flapping the reins, he urged Sula on. "Faster! Faster!" The reindeer responded, his feet seeming to float above the snow. Ross lost sight of the owl, but there was something else there now, something dark, slipping among the trees. He hoped he had imagined it. They were going too quickly to be certain.

Ahead lay a tall rock where the track forked. One way led up to the hilltop but Sula dived to the left, taking the downward path. Surviving a sharp turn in a flurry of white, they hurtled down the slope. The way here was bumpy, with small shrubs under the snow. As they bounced over humps and crashed into hollows, it felt as though the sled would be shaken to bits.

Suddenly there was a loud groan, like something in terrible pain. With a crackling of branches, a tree torn from its companions was thrown across their path, sending up a curtain of powdery snow. There was no time to stop. Before Ross realised what was happening, Sula was sailing into the air dragging the sled across the trunk. All he could do was to cling on.

On the other side lay a hollow where wind-blown snow had drifted. Sula landed in powder well past his belly. The sled ended up nose down in the drift, its runners resting against the fallen trunk. Ross had no choice but to slide off into the snow. Now both of them were stuck.

The grey owl was enjoying their predicament. Ross could see him, perched on a branch. "Take it easy," he called, "No rush." At the foot of the same tree stood a dark, hulking shape, like a fighting dog with thick, short legs. The broad head and heavy muzzle could have belonged to a small bear. But this was neither dog nor bear. Whatever it was, it stirred an ancient terror in the deepest part of his being. Ross thrust his hands into the snowdrift, trying to feel for the edge of the hollow.

"Leaving already?" the owl asked in his sardonic way. "What a shame. My friends would like to meet you." With great deliberation, the hulking shape took a few steps forward. Ross couldn't see its eyes, but he knew they were fastened on the deer. As if this were not terrible enough, two others fell in behind it. They were smaller, younger, but no less fearsome. "A little family, out foraging. Your deer will be a welcome snack."

The frightened reindeer struggled in the drift, rolling his eyes and bleating pitifully. His breath rose in a cloud. "It's all right, Sula, I'm here," Ross said, feeling not too brave himself.

"Look at those strong jaws," the owl said, lazily stretching one wing. "Ruthless scavengers. They haven't eaten for a while, so they are quite peckish."

Ross had to do something. With an effort, he managed to raise the front of the sled clear of the snow. But the runners were snagged on the stub of a broken branch. As he let go of the sled it slipped sideways, striking one shaft against the reindeer's hindquarters. Fearing he was under attack, Sula shook violently, and thrashed the snow with his antlers.

The owl took off, gliding silently to another tree. "Your deer has no chance," he said. "Lay my feather on the snow, and I will call them back."

There has to be a way out of this, Ross thought. If he could move some of the snow, Sula would manage the rest. Reindeer were brilliant at digging. First, he had to get in front of the deer. Forcing a way through the drift was tiring work, like wading through soft sand, but Ross kept going until his feet felt firmer ground. Keeping an eye on the antlers, he leaned in towards the deer's chest, and began to scoop away the powder with his mittens.

He worked furiously. Sweat trickled down his back as he tried to take out more snow than was sliding in. Sula was helping, but all the time the menacing creatures were coming nearer. They trotted a few paces, shaggy coats bouncing. Then paused with backs arched, bushy tails and heads down, to savour the scent of reindeer. They were moving again, closer and closer. Ross tried not to look at their vicious teeth, or their long, curved claws.

The owl left its perch to swoop low over his head. "Think about it, thief. Your reindeer is going to die. It will be messy. And it will be your fault."

Ross shifted more snow. If this didn't work, he thought, there was always Tilda's knife. But there were three of them, armed with teeth that could crush rocks. He would have to kill them all. What if he wasn't quick enough? The whole idea made him feel sick. Ross kept scooping. Sula had another hoof free.

"All I want is the feather. Not you, or your reindeer." The voice was fainter, almost plaintive. Maybe the owl was tiring. Maybe his power was waning. Ross paused to glance up. The owl was not there. Something flashed by – his eyes followed it to the front of the sled, where the letter R glowed like molten lava.

"You made it easy." The owl didn't sound feeble now. "Cut its skin. Breached its shield. What will Rymi say to that?"

Ross looked on in horror as the wooden struts began to swell. Long dried-up sap boiled and bubbled. Rymi's sled twisted and writhed, a demented monster. Even the scavengers recoiled from the sight. Snorting with alarm, Sula kicked with his hind legs and lurched forward out of the drift, pushing Ross aside. He knew he had to move quickly. Even the bravest reindeer has limits.

Ignoring the glowing, wriggling sled, Ross seized the knife. One swift cut severed the strap that bound shaft to collar. Then he was throwing himself across the reindeer's back, to slice the strap on the other side. Free at last, Sula fled down the slope with Ross clinging on as best he could.

Doubled over, with feet and head on opposite sides, snow and flashing hooves were all that Ross could see. One hand still clutched Tilda's knife, the other was gripping Sula's collar. He managed to get a foot on the reindeer's back, and in a few more strides he was dragging himself upright.

Barely slackening his pace, Sula jolted Ross forward until he was almost sitting on the reindeer's shoulders. This was more comfortable for both of them, although it was difficult for Ross to keep his balance. The only animal he'd ridden before was a beach donkey, and he only knew that because he'd seen the pictures. He held tight to Sula's collar, hoping he wouldn't fall off.

Once he felt more secure Ross replaced the knife, and glanced behind to check the track. There was no sign of the owl. But then his heart sank. The savage-looking scavengers were bounding after them. They weren't giving up, not until they had eaten something.

That gave Ross an idea. He would give them what they wanted. From out of the bag he took Hirta's dried meat, and tossed the food to the ground. Snarling and growling broke out as the three stopped to fight over their prize. That could have been Sula's fate. Ross stroked the reindeer's neck until the sounds were left far behind them.

For a while the pacing reindeer was the only movement in the forest. Then unearthly yellows and greens began to flicker across the snow. The torches of the Wayfinders were lighting their way home.

11

The Way of the North Wind

Sula was moving so slowly that the journey back seemed to go on forever. Frozen sweat chilled Ross's back, draining his energy further. His breath turned to frost on his chin. He thought of Hirta's dried meat with longing. She was right. He was starving. If only he he'd kept one piece.

Ross gazed dreamily at the colours sweeping through the trees, but even the lure of the aurora was not enough to keep him awake. Soon the forest dwindled to the space between Sula's antlers. Finally, lulled by the rhythm of the plodding reindeer, Ross's head drooped down onto his chest.

After a while he became aware that the plodding had stopped. Sula wasn't moving. Wearily, he tried to focus on the track ahead. There, ahead of them, stood a life-sized snowman.

Ross rubbed his eyes, and looked again. That was no snowman. A tall hooded figure was wrapped in white fur that spilled onto the surrounding snow. On one shoulder sat a raven, its black feathers gleaming with a purplish sheen. The shades of forest animals slipped from the folds of the robe, only to vanish again. Ross saw hare, fox, snow grouse, wolf, lynx, and others he could not name. In its arms the vision cradled a birch basket, heaped with red berries.

"*All those will find me, who follow the way of the north wind.*"

Hearing that made his heart feel lighter, although he did not know why. Ross stared dreamily as the raven tugged at the hood, unveiling a face bright as the full moon, and a tangle of hair that was silver as frosted branches.

"*Eat, wanderer.*"

She offered up the basket, allowing a beam from the Lights to fall across the fruit. The berries glowed with an inner fire. They spoke of warmth, happiness, and jam on toast.

As Ross reached out a hand, the raven hopped from her shoulder. It picked out a cluster of berries, and glided towards him, landing on his outstretched arm. The bird was heavy, with a fighter's thick neck. He felt the strong grip of its claws through his sleeve, flinched at the bristling throat hackles and the red-rimmed eye so close to his own. Then he took the berries from its powerful beak, and squashed them into his mouth.

~

The next sound Ross heard was the clonk of a reindeer bell. Dogs barked, jolting him awake. Wood smoke tingled in his nose. They were home. Exhausted, he slid off the reindeer, and flopped down in the snow.

Hirta rushed over to scoop him up, while Larna and Fann whined and yapped with excitement. "You brave lad," she said, pulling Ross to his feet and hugging him. "Oh, you look exhausted."

"I'm alright," he whispered. "How's Tilda?"

He hardly needed to ask. The answer shone from Hirta's face. She told him to come and see for himself, but Ross broke free from her, and throwing his arms around Sula's neck, he buried his face in the reindeer's thick hair. "You're the best," he said. "A real hero."

"Leave him to me," Hirta said, taking Ross firmly by the arm. "He needs rest. So do you." She steered Ross towards the tent, opened the door, and pushed him inside.

It felt so good to hear the slap of the door, to breathe in the smells, to feel warmth folding around him again. Tilda was still in her bed. When she saw him she raised herself up, murmuring sleepily, "You are here. All is well. Nanna told me what you did." Then she sank back under the reindeer hides.

Ross remembered the owl's feather. It wasn't right for it to be in the same place as Tilda. So, although he didn't feel like it he went out again, dragging his feet through the snow to the other tent.

Rymi was sitting by the fire with a reindeer hide draped around his shoulders. He looked desperately tired, every year of his life etched deep into his face. Even smoking his pipe seemed an effort of will. "You did well, Ross," he said, placing the pipe on a hearthstone. "A young stranger no longer. You are one of us now."

He motioned for Ross to sit down, and handed him a bowl. When Ross had gulped down the brew, Rymi asked if he had brought the feather. Ross reached into his bag, only too happy to give it up. "No need to tell Hirta," Rymi said, with a faint smile. He wrapped the feather neatly, and tucked it into the pocket of his coat, which was serving as a pillow. "At last. Now I can rest." Without another word, he knocked the pipe out on the stone, and curled up on his side like a cat.

Back in the other tent, Ross unfastened the knife belt, and placed it on the bed beside Tilda. Then he settled himself by the hearth with a pelt across his shoulders. Meat sizzled in the frying pan, while the glow from the logs suggested all was well with the firesprite.

Tilda slept on. Ross, too, was dozing by the time Hirta returned. "Your hero is comfortable," she said, eyeing the severed straps as she hung up Sula's harness. "Where have you left the sled?"

A bowl of hot tea revived Ross enough to explain. "And after we got free from the drift, there wasn't time to eat." Hirta tut-tutted when she heard that, until he told her how the meat saved Sula's life.

"You did right," she said. "Wolverines usually eat corpses. They can even live off bones. But they know how to kill, oh yes." She curled her lip in disgust. "They bite the deer's throat. Hang on till it bleeds to death." Hirta put some fried meat into a bowl with a piece of warm bread. "After all that, you need feeding up."

Ross needed no encouragement. While he ate like a starving wolf, Hirta told him how Rymi was recovering, but would not want company for a while. Then exhausted but content, Ross fell into a deep sleep.

~

Ross awoke to a happy sound. Tilda's grandma was singing her joy as she shaped dough for the day's bread. Tilda knelt beside her with Larna's head resting on her lap, while the firesprite teased knots into the dog's feathery tail. A pleasing aroma drifted from the pot that was hanging over the fire. Ross yawned happily. Everything was back to normal.

"Now, young man," Hirta said cheerfully. "Ready for some food? We will eat soon."

Ross nodded. "I'll just go and see Sula, if that's alright."

He walked up the bank to the deer pen under a heavy sky dense with cloud. Snow drifted on the wind, dusting the reindeers' backs with white. They moved away as he came towards them, but Sula remained lying down with his legs tucked up. "Wish I had something for you," Ross said, kneeling in front of the deer. Sula's eyelids lifted, although his drooping head remained tilted with one antler resting in the snow.

"He is tired, that is all." Tilda came up beside them, carrying her bag of reindeer treats. "Here. This will help." Ross smiled awkwardly as he took the ball of lichen. What were you supposed to say to someone whose soul has been stolen?

"You alright, then?"

Tilda frowned. "I think so."

"What was it like? Were you scared?"

"At first."

Ross was in a quandary. He wanted to know every detail, yet at the same time he didn't want to hear.

"Everything felt different," Tilda continued. "Starlight felt like bathing in a cold lake. Soil was alive, breathing. Roots were reaching, touching..." She looked past Ross to the forest behind him, as though she were searching for something. Little dots of snow began to gather on her eyelashes. She didn't blink them away.

Ross cupped the lichen in both hands, and held it under Sula's nose. Something had changed. Maybe part of her was out there now, among the trees. But as the reindeer raised his head from the snow, the movement seemed to bring Tilda back. "Birch spirits, they were ... "

"Angry?"

"Curious. Watchful. I kept really still, so as not to annoy them. Oh, for so long. Then I heard Rymi calling. All that time there was nothing to see, nothing, and suddenly there was a beautiful white reindeer. Rymi was saying, 'Come home Tilda.' I floated out of the birch, how I do not know. Then I woke up, and there was Nanna, smiling and crying."

She had seen the white reindeer. Ross felt a tug in his chest. He concentrated on the softness of Sula's mouth as the deer nuzzled his palms. "It's over now, though."

"Is it? I still see those eyes. Owl eyes, cold and empty."

Ross thought of the tail feather, hidden in Rymi's coat. "Suppose that'll go away, in time." Tilda took a deep breath, and pulled her mouth into a sad smile. "What about you? When you found *him*?"

"We kept him busy, didn't we, Sula? Sula was brilliant. Wish he was my reindeer."

"He is a fine deer. Strong, and handsome."

"And he's not scared of anything," Ross added. "I couldn't have done it without him."

So admiring were they of Sula that neither of them noticed the approach of another reindeer, not until Tilda was pitched forward into the snow. The culprit looked on anxiously. "Miri! You are jealous," she said, laughing as she flicked snow from her face. In that instant, Ross saw the real Tilda again.

~

The next day Ross woke early, with an urge to explore outside. So while Hirta was emptying the night bucket he threw on his coat, and slung the half-moon bag across his chest. She had allowed him to keep the small bag, which was spacious enough for the phone. But that was safer in the inside pocket of his coat, leaving the bag for the pinecone, the pot of green eye stuff, and a silver coin he kept because it was so shiny. Before he left the tent Ross put some more ointment on his eye, then made sure the bag was properly closed with its antler toggle.

The snow showers had passed, leaving lakes of deepest ink among scattered charcoal clouds. Fann came to join him, and together they wandered among the trees. As the dog stopped to sniff at some yellow snow, Ross spotted a likely stick. "Here, Fann. Fetch." He was watching the dog ploughing through a drift when he noticed some trees with strips of hide around their trunks. One close to Hirta's tent, then another and another, they formed a short row leading off into the forest. At that moment he heard the creak of the tent door. Tilda emerged, carrying an antler and a length of branch.

"What are those for?" Ross asked, nodding toward the trees. By now he knew better than to point at things, especially when he didn't know what they were. Tilda stood beside him, and they watched a faint breeze twitch the ends of the strips. "Markers," she said. "To guide a lost soul home."

Suddenly Fann trotted between them, rapping their legs with his stout stick. "Bad dog," Ross said irritably. "He is only being himself," Tilda said, rolling her eyes. Fann, oblivious, settled in the snow to test the stick with his teeth. Tilda prodded Ross with the antler. "Lasso practise," she announced. "First, you will make fire."

Tilda planted the pine branch upright in the snow. From her belt pouch she took a short metal stick, a sharp-edged flint, and a ball of fuzz. She showed Ross how to hold the steel with its end in the tinder – "shredded birch bark, make sure it is dry" – then hit the steel with the strikestone. "Strike downwards. Keep doing it till a spark falls on the tinder. There! Quick, pick it up." Gingerly, Ross took the fuzz between his hands. "Blow on it. Gently." Ross grinned as the fibres glowed, and burst into life. "Good," Tilda said, gesturing at the pine branch. "Now light that roll of bark in the top."

Once the torch was blazing, the antler was placed a short distance away. Ross spent some time trying to lasso it. Eventually he managed a throw without catching himself, so Tilda challenged him to a contest. "Three throws each. See if you are as good as my brother."

"Your brother?"

Tilda smiled. "Those are his leggings you are wearing."

Ross made his first competitive throw. "Why isn't he here?" he asked, wondering if her brother would mind about the leggings. The loop came down to one side, catching one of the antler's points. That counted.

"He's with Ma and Fa, in the settlement," Tilda replied. Ross stared at her in astonishment. "What, like a village? Is it far?" Tilda said it was a few camps away. Ross asked why she was not there. "I was, for a while," she said, coiling the lasso. "I missed the forest."

"Don't you miss your family?"

Tilda stared at him. "Your Ma, who gave you a scrystone, do you miss her?"

Ross realised that he hadn't thought of her for ages. Guiltily, he scuffed the snow with his boots as Tilda's throw dropped neatly over the target. "I like it here," she told him. "Anyway, someone has to look after Nanna. She will never leave the forest." She reached out to turn Ross's face towards the torchlight. "That eye is bruised."

"It's nothing. Rymi gave me some stuff for it."

"He is known for his potions, "Tilda said. "It will work, I am sure."

Suddenly there was rustling, and the swish of snow falling. As they turned to look, a raven came down out of the trees, snatched Fann's stick from between his paws, and flew with it to a nearby branch. There it sat in full view, brazenly twiddling the stick in its beak, as Fann leapt up and down, barking helplessly.

"Crazy bird," Ross grinned, admiring its nerve. But Tilda felt for her reindeer amulet. "Ravens are not like other birds," she said darkly. This was an omen – that was certain – but whether for good or ill she could not decide.

~

During those two days Rymi slept for most of the time. When he did leave his tent he returned quickly, and was soon asleep again. Hirta visited frequently, growing increasingly anxious. She fussed around him with tea and food, but usually he waved her away. "Leave me alone, woman," he would say, irritably. "Let me rest."

After one of these exchanges, Hirta confided in Tilda and Ross. "I worry. He is not well. I fear all this has been too much."

"Of course you worry," Tilda said. "He is a friend, from long ago."

"Since we were old enough to fetch wood. We were always together. That was before the spirits called him." A shadow crossed Hirta's face, and she touched her bear's tooth amulet.

"Suppose that changed everything," Tilda said.

Hirta gave a shy smile. "Even then I thought, one day…"

"Nanna!" Tilda pretended to be shocked. "What about elder-Fa?"

"Oh, that was before your elder-Fa. I am surprised you remember him. You were very small when he passed."

"I remember he made me laugh, with his stories."

"Yes, he was a kind man." Hirta blinked the mist from her eyes. "When your mother came along, he was so happy."

Ross squirmed. This was beyond embarrassing. Anyway he didn't want Hirta to be miserable, not now everything was all right. Then he remembered what grandparents love to talk about. So, with what he hoped was a sympathetic expression, he asked, "What was it like in the olden times?"

Hirta rallied immediately. "Not as it is now," she replied. "When I was your age – yes, cheeky pup, I was young once – we all followed the reindeer. We went with them to their summer places on the hills. We went with them to their winter places in the forest. Life was hard, but we were a strong family. And our gods were kind. They gave us all we needed."

"Did you have fun?"

"Fun?" Hirta looked at him oddly, as though the word had no meaning. "Well, we sang, and sometimes we danced, if that is what you mean. And the old stories, oh, we loved them. I can see it now, the great gathering, when everyone came together at leaf fall. Us little ones sitting at the front, watching our Fas tell a story. The Wrong Mushrooms, that was a good one. They played all the characters, you see. Rymi always laughed at that, it was his favourite."

"Isn't it like that now?" Ross said.

"Nothing is the same, now they are settled. They have this horrible drink…what is it, Tilda?"

"Coffee."

"Hmm. Coffee," Hirta repeated, wrinkling her nose. She picked up a stick, and annoyed the fire until a cloud of irritable sparks rose from it. "Oh, I could have a little cabin, if I wanted. Two rooms, an outside privy… I would fill it with things, and keep it just so, and then the cabin would be my master. I would never be free."

"All we need is here," Tilda said. "The reindeer, the forest."

"That is a true thing. Whatever we need, we can make. Except for rye flour. We barter hides for that."

"And tea, Nanna." Tilda raised an amused eyebrow at Ross. "We must have tea."

"I could do without," Hirta replied, boldly. "I know which leaves to make tea from, and how to make flour with birch pith. The forest provides, if you know where to look." She gave a huge yawn. "Now, you two– Bed."

~

Later, as everyone slept, Ross was snared in a nightmare.

His dream was filled with shadows. In those shadows were eyeless faces, watching. Then light – a pool, where green water shimmered like the Wayfinders' fire. While he was gazing into the water an unseen force threw him in, and he was swimming in green fire, round and round, round and round. Ahead of him were others, arms and legs flailing, paddling madly. Ross knew them. They were all him. Then something came, and scooped them all out, setting them down by a tree in the forest. Now he was one again. The tree shifted, and it was a woman with berries, and stars in her hair...

Sweating, he pushed aside the reindeer hides. The fire was blazing. Hirta was snoring – she must have piled on the logs, then gone back to sleep. Ross wanted to ask her about the green fire. Why was he having these weird dreams? What if they weren't dreams?

He was wide-awake now, but it wasn't fair to disturb the others. So he stared into the fire's heart, where wood transforms into pure, searing heat. The firesprite appeared, hovering in the smoke. It winked at him. Then it sent shadows flickering across the wall, shadows of wild beasts dancing like people.

Maybe Rymi was awake too, staring at his fire. What did he see? He could read minds. Rescue souls. Travel to other worlds. And then Ross thought – I travelled to another world. I came here, flew here, with the white reindeer. What does that make me?

12

The Great Reindeer

Tilda gripped the meat between her teeth, slicing off a piece with an easy twist of her knife. Ross, chewing laboriously on his breakfast meat, watched the blade with envious eyes. "I used it to cut Sula free," he said. "It might be a bit blunt."

"Not now," Tilda replied. She sliced again with an exaggerated movement, jabbing Ross's elbow and sending his strip of meat flying. Fann was there in a flash. With one snap of white teeth, the last of Ross's breakfast was in the dog's stomach.

There was not much room in the tent, now that they were four. Worn down by Hirta's persistence, Rymi had agreed to join them. Then there were the dogs. Although they were working dogs they behaved like pets around the hearth, pushing their muzzles underneath arms, trying to climb on everyone's knee.

Hirta should have been pleased with her success, but after a restless night she was not in a good mood. In the struggle to unhook the kettle from its chain she almost dropped it into the fire. When she tried to kneel down again, Larna was stretched out in her place. "You two are spoiling these dogs," she grumbled, "giving them treats, letting them do as they please."

Ross scowled. That wasn't fair. Tilda grinned mischievously. "If I spill this on the fire," Hirta snapped, "nobody will be laughing."

"Sorry Nanna."

While Tilda ushered Larna away, Hirta rested the kettle on a hearthstone. It was Rymi's turn to feel her wrath. "Who is wishing these ills on us? I want to know," she said, jabbing the air with the potholder. "Tell me the truth."

Rymi wiped the blade of his knife on the top of his boot. He didn't look up. "Truth? Truth is a dream," he murmured, turning the knife slowly this way and that, watching the reflections of firelight in the metal. Hirta glared at him. "Here is a truth – a terrible thing happened, and you know why."

"A thing does not have to happen, for it to be true."

"Know what I think?" Hirta said, rolling her eyes, "You see too much. More than is good for you."

"Truer than you know," Rymi replied. Then, noticing she was at boiling point, he added hastily, "Your heart speaks, so I will answer."

Hirta was taken aback. She had not expected him to give in so easily. Hurriedly she poured their tea then settled down to listen, sipping from her drinking bowl. Ross balanced his bowl on his knees, blowing on the liquid to cool it. Tilda encouraged Larna onto her lap, and hugged the dog close. They waited, expectantly.

"Many stars have fallen since this began," Rymi said. "Once, in the long day, a stranger came, a seeker after knowledge. Kelvan, he called himself. At first, all was well. He tended the drum and fire while I visited the Old Ones.

The things they taught I passed on to him. Kelvan was keen to learn, had an easy way with people."

"I heard right, then," Hirta said. "You did have an apprentice."

"He had the makings of a healer. But something was lacking – humility. I thought, as he learns more he will find wisdom." Rymi gave her a rueful look. "The one who sees does not see everything."

"Things in front of our eyes are the hardest to see," Hirta muttered under her breath.

"I told him, the craft must only be used for good. But his first spirit-flight made him far worse. He found pleasure in wrongdoing, following me into other worlds, looking to interfere. The spirits were angry. I had to send Kelvan away."

Hirta nodded. "Ah. A grudge."

"This story is not ended." For a while Rymi seemed mesmerised by the hearth, where the last bits of a log were crumbling to ash. When he spoke again it was with regret. "Kelvan could have helped our folk, had a good life, if he had been content."

"A hard path, the healer's life," Hirta commented. "Not for everyone."

"That may be, but our elders have gone before. They have trodden on every stone. Yet Kelvan knew better. Followed his own path…" There was an even longer pause, as Rymi followed the demise of the log. "He fell in with a sorcerer, a binder of souls. I could do nothing."

Hirta cleared her throat. She said she was sure he did all he could. "Decay attracts decay," Rymi replied wearily. "So it was with Kelvan."

This is a trial for him, Hirta thought. He should be resting. She reached for the kettle, suggesting more tea.

But Rymi would not be distracted, even though his head still ached from the trance, and his memories were misted by shadows. He began again, holding up a hand to deter further interruptions.

"He was a man once, this soul-binder. In a vision he saw his own life's end. This is a burden for all who see. Except him – he planned to cheat death. He drew out Kelvan's souls, and gave them instead of his own. Even Kelvan's likeness, the sorcerer took that, as carelessly as he puts on owl's feathers. All this, the spirits showed me. That sorcerer became a malignant spirit, a demon preying on souls. Each soul brings him power. And so he grows stronger."

Hirta clutched at her bear's tooth. "Preying on souls? Old Ones keep us."

"For the stolen, there is no peace," Rymi said.

"I saw them," Ross said. "Looking like ghosts. If Tilda hadn't come–"

"You would be among the lost," Rymi replied. "More power for him, a blow struck at me. The soul-binder mistook you for my new apprentice."

"And me? Why did he take me?" Tilda whispered, clutching Larna so tightly that the dog began to whine.

"He knew I would come for you, Tilda. The ill he has done you – and you, Ross – was all aimed at me. He sees a tired old man. He thinks to weaken me."

Ross scratched his head thoughtfully, remembering the man in grey fur he'd met by the den. That must have been the apprentice, Kelvan. Or rather his appearance, shrugged on like old clothes. This sorcerer was ruthless all right. And now he was coming after Rymi. "Why does he hate you?" Ross asked.

Rymi hesitated, considering his words. "There is something I must do. He is determined to stop me." Ross was about to ask, what is it you have to do, when Hirta cut in. "We are all in danger now. We have to get away."

"Nanna, he will find us wherever we go," Tilda said, sadly.

"I know, I know. But can we feel safe here?"

"Tilda speaks wisely," Rymi said. "If I am to protect you, we must all stay together."

Ross had a suggestion. "What about the village? We could go there."

Hirta and Tilda looked at each other, uneasily. Rymi gazed at Ross across the dwindling hearth-fire. "Unwise," he said. "Strangers there, they... They do not approve of my calling. They have no respect for the Old Ones."

"They would take your drum, and burn it. And you with it," Hirta said, bluntly. "That is the truth."

"They say we are wrong to follow the path," Rymi continued. "How is it wrong to honour the gods of our elders? They are all around, in the singing wind, in every rock and stream. It has always been so." The herders muttered their agreement. Then Hirta turned to Ross, her eyes shining with the last flicker of flame. "What do you think they would make of you, those strangers?" she said. "A lad who fell out of a snow-cloud?" Smarting under her stare, Ross gazed at his boots. His suggestion had stirred up something he didn't understand, but the passion in their voices spoke clearly enough.

"Shadows pass," Rymi said, attempting some words of comfort. "We are safe from them here, in the forest." Safe from them, Ross thought, but not safe from the soul-binder.

For a while they watched the spent logs as one after another, they settled into silken flakes. No one spoke. No one moved to revive the fire. Then suddenly Rymi said,

"What should we do, Tilda?" They waited for her answer, their faces drained of colour by the gloom. "The herd will move soon," she told them. "They will head for the lake, where the lichen is fresh."

"There. It is settled," Rymi said. "You will come to my camp."

~

Once the decision had been made, things moved quickly. Dismantling Rymi's tent, and packing his few belongings, was swiftly completed. Hirta had much more to do. First she had to soothe the firesprite. "Your family needs you, hearth-keeper," she said, pleading with it to accompany them. After gaining its agreement, she packed some live embers into a box lined with moss. Then she took the guardian figure from the tent pole, and wrapped it carefully. While she was doing that, the others were outside clearing snow from the sleds, and pushing them onto the track. The dogs helped by running to and fro, and getting in the way. Then Hirta doused what was left of the fire, and everyone was needed in the tent.

Reindeer skins were rolled, and spare clothes stuffed into deerskin bags. Bowls, bags, and birch-bark boxes were put on a sled with built up sides, along with the cauldron, frying pan, hatchet, and kettle. Joints of frozen meat appeared, retrieved from a small, stone chamber under the snow. Lastly, Hirta carried out the shiny hearthstone nestled inside its own deerskin pouch, and placed it, with its precious resident, inside the cooking pot.

Now only the tent itself remained. The A-framed door was unfastened, and every deerskin untied from the tent poles. After skins and poles had been piled on two sledges, the draught reindeer were brought from their pen.

Ross waited with Miri while the others harnessed reindeer to the loaded sleds. A long tether fastened each deer to the back of the sled in front, so that none of them needed a driver. Finally Hirta fetched Old Olli with the square bell around his neck, and tied him behind the last sled.

"The herd will hear it, and follow Olli," Rymi explained, stowing his bag on Miri's sled. Then he led up his own reindeer, and hitched him to the back. "Sula has earned his rest, I think. No work for him." Ross caught the reindeer's eye, and for a moment they were together again, running over the snow under the torches of the Wayfinders. This sparked an uncomfortable memory. "Your sled," Ross mumbled, "sorry about that."

"It was an old friend," Rymi said. "But I will build another. You are safe, that is what matters."

With everything loaded, they were ready to go. Ross gazed sadly at the empty camp. A ring of hearthstones amid trampled branches was all that was left of their home. But while he was unsettled, the others thought little of it. This was their life, striking camp, and moving on.

They started off through the forest in the brief glow of twilight, with Hirta driving the leading sled. Ross rode on the last one, watching Olli walking behind. "Keep an eye on the herd," she told him. "Call out if something goes wrong."

Tilda was going to walk with the dogs while Rymi drove her sled. They hung back, leaving a gap for the reindeer that were expected to come from the forest. Miri, desperate to follow the others, jinked from side to side. Rymi had to hold him back until Olli's white rump vanished around the first bend.

Before long Ross saw the first of the herd, summoned by Olli's bell. The animals hesitated, peering from among the trees, until an old female jumped out onto the track. After that they came eagerly – cream-coated, fawn-coated, nut-brown faces, peat-brown faces, some with white blazes or stars. Ross laughed to see them all following Olli with his clonking bell, and funny spectacled face.

At the rear of the procession, Rymi halted the sled to let more deer join. Tilda knew every one of them, even though the herd was a hundred strong. Familiar sounds, the clicking, creaking and barking, made her feel happy again. Yet the moment was fleeting. All too soon, Rymi reminded her of something she wanted to forget.

"We should talk, Tilda, even though it is difficult."

Tilda could see a young deer in trouble. The dogs were gathering up stragglers, something they did without being told, but amidst all the fuss a calf had stumbled into a pocket of deep snow. It stood there, bewildered. "A wound must be cleaned before it can heal," Rymi called, as she set off to help. Tilda knew this was true. He had freed her stolen soul, made her whole again, and for that – well, what she felt could fill the sky. Yet his closeness to the spirits, once so reassuring, now reminded her of the soul-binder.

When Tilda reached the calf it was trembling. Wrapping one arm around its hindquarters, she gave it a good shove with her shoulder. The startled animal scrambled out, shook itself, and ran to join the other reindeer.

Tilda flicked the black pellets off her sleeve, thinking how fragile life was. That half-grown calf, only eight moons old – would she survive the long night? And their old bull – life had certainly changed for him. Barely two moons ago he was proud and strong, fighting off young rivals. Now, with his antlers gone, even the calves failed to respect him. As Tilda turned away she saw the old bull stumble, pushed off the track by a cow.

Her thoughts were churning as she came up behind the sled. "Talking is difficult? Feeling lost was difficult," she said, addressing Rymi's back. "Thinking I would never see our hearth-fire again."

Rymi was watching the herd, elbows resting on his knees, Miri's reins held tightly in one hand. Annoyed, she willed him to turn, or say something, but instead he relaxed the reins, and the sled set off with a lurch. As if for the first time, Tilda noticed his hat. It was white fox. So white that it seemed to radiate light. The bushy tail, fastened to the top, flipped from side to side with every movement of the sled.

Tilda tried again. "The birch spirits..." She faltered, unnerved by the wagging foxtail. She had not forgotten Nanna's dream, the white fox's warning. "They did me no harm. But...it was... Oh, no use," she said irritably, wondering if he was even listening. "I have no words."

"I understand," Rymi said, over his shoulder.

"Do you? They never let go. They reach into my head." She walked faster, pulling her shawl close around her neck, until she came level with him. "It is happening now, even with the herd."

"Do not fear this, Tilda, it is a blessing. Trees have wisdom."

His words only served to stir her anger. "This is my fate? For ever?" She seized Rymi's arm, forcing him to halt the sled. "Make them leave me alone."

"Impossible," he replied, with disarming honesty. "But when they trouble you it is better not to fight them. Let their thoughts drift from your mind, like leaves carried away on the wind. Practise, until it becomes easy."

Suddenly aware of showing disrespect, Tilda let go of his arm. Yet the fire still burned in her eyes. "I need you to help me."

Rymi nodded. "When our hearths are warm, I will make you a powerful amulet."

~

When Hirta and Ross reached the frozen lake the herd spread out around them, circling among the trees. "I knew it," she said, "they will never go across. They smell wolf." The swirling bodies parted as the others came through. Rymi called out, "What is the matter?"

"That wolf of yours. They know it is there."

"Let me go first, with Sula."

So Sula was put in place of Miri. While Rymi drove across the ice, the others watched from the bank. Everything white looked as blue as the twilight, so it was impossible to distinguish the wolf from the snow – until the wolf moved.

"Put a leash on this dog," Hirta shouted, catching Fann by the scruff as he made a dash for the lake. Calmly, the wolf watched the sled as it came up the bank, and into the camp. "You see?" she said. "Not like a dog. A dog would be jumping all over."

Even when Rymi walked towards him, the wolf showed no sign of excitement. But as he drew near Lumi came forward to have his ears rubbed. There followed a curious little dance as the wolf circled Rymi, brushing against the man's boots, and weaving his head from side to side like the silliest cub.

"It looks tame enough," Hirta said grudgingly, "but I would not trust it." Secretly she marvelled at his empathy with the wolf, although she could never admit it.

Eventually man and wolf melted into the trees. "We can go now," Tilda said, but Hirta disagreed. "The herd will not move, not after seeing that creature. Leave them here, until we see how things work out. Olli can stay with them, to keep them together."

When all the sleds had come across the draught reindeer were tethered among the trees. They were not at all happy at first, fearing the wolf was near, but Sula's example helped to calm them. With the dogs on guard the reindeer settled down to dig, sending snow in all directions.

After Hirta had surveyed the standing tent poles and declared them to be acceptable, the skins were unrolled, pushed up, and secured. Tilda and Ross attached the triangular door, and went off to cut some branches for the floor. Meanwhile Hirta hung up the guardian, giving it a quick polish with her skirt. Then she scraped loose snow from the ring of old hearthstones, and swept it out of the tent.

On their return, Tilda and Ross joined Hirta in packing down the remaining snow on the floor. Round and round they went, stamping hard with their boots. For some reason this reduced them all to helpless laughter. Then they covered the floor with fresh spruce, tucking in all the ends. Once reindeer hides had been spread out, and their belongings brought in, the tent looked homely once more.

They were admiring their efforts when Rymi appeared in the open door. "Plenty of wood in the stack, help yourselves," he said. "Do not mind Lumi. He knows to keep away from reindeer."

"He has to eat something," Hirta grumbled.

"Lumi prefers fish," Rymi told her. "And I have plenty of fish."

"Hmm. We'll see." Hirta was not convinced. With a shake of his head, Rymi was gone. "Come back later," she shouted after him, "when the food is ready."

With the floor covered, Hirta could kneel in comfort before the hearth. She took the shiny stone from its pouch, and removing one of the old ones, placed it in the space with great ceremony. After stroking it, and saying the words of welcome to the hearth-keeper, she unpacked the embers from their nest of moss. Soon she had the fire crackling into life. Smoke billowed around the black kettle, filling the tent, and making their eyes smart. But as the air warmed, the choking layer was driven up towards the smoke-hole, leaving clear air below. When the brief twilight turned into night, the three were snug in their own space again.

While Hirta prepared the meal, Tilda and Ross went outside. They untied the dogs, and led them around the camp in the starlight, allowing them to sniff at all the wolf scents. Larna paid particular attention to the hut. "Not easy for them with Lumi here," Tilda said.

Ross was still buzzing. "Today was amazing, the herd and everything. And the tent, it's just the same." Tilda smiled. "We have done this before, a few times."

They lingered on the bank to watch the sky deepening to inky black. Across the lake, from the darkened forest, came the sound of Olli's herd-bell. Above the treetops a faint, white mist was shivering against the stars. Glimmers of green slid from the white, turning to yellow as they went. Glowing green rays swayed across the sky, colouring the snow on the fells beyond. Almost as quickly they vanished into the darkness.

While Ross brooded on the Lights, and the strange feelings they stirred in him, Tilda turned to the stars that shone above Rymi's hut. "Look, the Great Reindeer. There, in the stardrift." Ross looked. He shook his head at the crowded sky, where the galaxy gleamed like a river of crushed pearls. He couldn't see anything that looked like a reindeer. Tilda bent down, and drew a loose "W" in the snow. "His antlers," she said.

"That's Cassiopeia."

"Is it? See the rest of him, underneath." Tilda was being careful not to point. "And over there."

The Great Reindeer was a huge constellation, Cassiopeia, Perseus, and Auriga combined. Yet the old names no longer seemed right. What else could it be, but a reindeer? Now that he had seen it, Ross knew he'd never think of it in any other way. "Looks like he's dancing," he said, grinning.

Firelight shone across the snow as Rymi opened his door. He stepped out of the hut, fastening his coat. "We're watching the Great Reindeer," Ross said.

Rymi came over to stand between them, and the three gazed at the star-group that dominated the hump-backed hill. The infinity of the sky was overwhelming. They stood for a while, awed by the glittering multitude. Then Rymi said, "You know that place, Tilda." She gave Rymi a sidelong look. Of course she knew. "It's shining fell. Where the ones who see go into the hill."

"See that star, Ross," Rymi said, "that star in the Reindeer's hoof – how it almost touches the hill. One more circle in the star-dance, and the Great Reindeer will step onto shining fell. And see there, the Seven, near Steadfast. Soon the long night will be at its darkest. Do you know what that means?"

Ross knew. "It's the solstice. Midwinter. After that, the days get longer. I mean," he added quickly, remembering where he was, "the Sun starts to come back."

"The eternal one's journey is a mystery," Rymi said. "When he leaves, our hearts cry. We fear he will never come back. But there is hope – words, handed down. This is how I heard them, long ago." He raised his hands, palms facing the sky, and spoke in the voice of the elders…

Sun, Fa, far from us
we are beyond your circle of fire
in the long night, your song in the hearth-flame
you are hidden yet rise in our hearts
in the wolf moon you will return to us
drive away darkness, chase away cold
bright the stars who sing your story
bright the torch that lights your way

Ross wanted to ask, how could anything light the way for the Sun? But the silence was heavy with the presence of old souls, so he did not dare.

Finally Rymi bowed his head. The ancestors drew back, and he was himself again, smiling and clapping them both on the shoulder. "We should go in," he said. "Hirta will be annoyed if we let her food spoil." Ross nodded eagerly. He was hungry enough to eat the tent door.

They piled into the warmth, where the smell of frying was so good that it made Ross feel light-headed. Happily, Hirta's black pudding, dried mushrooms, and berry relish did not disappoint. When they had finished she put thin rounds of dough into the frying pan – there hadn't been time to bake on the stones – and made a kind of pancake for each of them. Then she brought out one of her birch boxes, saying, "We deserve a treat. This is just the thing."

Tilda and Rymi made appreciative noises as the pancakes were handed out. Ross wrinkled his nose, suspecting that their idea of a treat might be different from his – liver maybe, or something made from fishes' insides.

First, the shiny hearthstone received its share. Rymi was served next and then Tilda. By now Ross could hardly wait, but at last Hirta spooned the golden fruit onto his pancake. Jam! Ross rolled up the pancake, and bit off one end. The glistening berries tasted a bit like custard. He took another bite, very slowly. From the corner of his eye he saw the firesprite on its stone, scooping liquid sunshine into its fluttering hands.

13

The Nature of Dreams

Rymi, carrying a bucket, led them down a narrow track behind his hut. It curved among spruces to a low bank clothed in willow scrub, where a shelf of frozen turf overhung bare rock. They heard the soft splashing of water. Bubbling up from deep underground, squeezing through a fissure in the rock, it trickled into a stone bowl then overflowed into the pool below. Thick ice had formed across most of the surface, yet that end of the pool was mysteriously unfrozen. Gathered around, gazing reverently at the dark, glassy surface, they marvelled at the sound of freely running water.

"It makes me think of leafing, hearing that," Hirta whispered. "You say it never freezes?"

"Never," Rymi said.

Tilda was puzzled. "The path is familiar," she said, "but not this pool."

"Few know it," Rymi replied, with a secretive smile. "The Old Ones keep it hidden."

The oldest spruce in the grove stood nearby. A majestic tree, it was dressed with a variety of treasures. Most of the objects dangling from its branches were antler carvings, but more than a few had the tawny glow of tarnished silver.

"This is a place of wonder," Hirta said. "We should make offerings." She took off one of her leather bracelets, and fastened it around one of the lower branches. Tilda's contribution was an antler-tip pendant. They turned to Ross, nodding meaningfully.

He had nothing to give. Except... Slowly, he took the small silver coin from his pocket. Once he wouldn't have given it a thought. Now, like the phone, it was a link with his old life, proof that his memories were more than dreams. He rubbed the shiny metal between his fingers, reluctant to give it up. But that was the point. An offering had to be something that mattered.

Tilda spoke to the tree, saying, "Accept our gifts, keeper of the spring." She made a small cut near the end of a branch, and Ross stepped forward to slide his coin into the notch. Then Hirta and Rymi dipped ladles into the pool, sending ripples across the surface. As they left the spring with brimming buckets, Ross glanced back at his coin. It was gleaming softly, a tiny crescent moon above the deep, dark water.

~

While Tilda and her grandma disappeared into their tent, Ross hung back. He watched Rymi set down his bucket, take wood from the stack, and go into the hut leaving his water outside. Ross knew that it would freeze if it remained there. He walked over, and saw ice already forming.

"Your water's here," he called. "Shall I bring it in?"

Rymi said yes. Ross carried the bucket inside, put it down, and turned to go. Then he hesitated, his hand on the half-open door. Rymi looked up from raking the hearth. "What was that?" he asked.

"I didn't say anything."

"You wanted to."

Ross let the door close. "There is something…"

"I am listening."

"It's this really weird dream," Ross said, shuffling his feet in embarrassment. Most people would groan when they heard that, but Rymi didn't seem to mind. "Better sit down, then," he said, indicating a place by the fire.

Ross liked the turf hut. It resembled the tent with its smells of wood smoke, crushed pine, and well-worn deer hides. But it was larger than the tent, and the curving roof made it look like a cave. It felt more homely than on his first visit, when the air had been charged with the presence of the white reindeer, and the eerie cries of spirit birds. Ross smiled as he remembered his previous self. How little he knew then.

"A deep matter, the nature of dreams," Rymi said, ladling water from the bucket into the kettle. He snapped some branches, and added them to the fire, before settling by the hearth. "Many a dream is just a dream. It does not belong to past or present. It is, or is not. Then there are other dreams…"

Ross frowned. This wasn't going to be easy.

"I told you how this world is one of many. Remember? Most of us will never see, or even sense, those other worlds. Yet they are near. Like different currents in a river – slow near the banks, rushing in the middle – that is how the worlds are to each other."

In that moment, Ross saw the truth. All the things he thought he knew, all the certainties that divided him from those other worlds, were stripped away. He felt the presence of places he could never know. But the revelation was too much. He covered his face with his hands. When he peered between spread fingers, he was relieved to see nothing but bright flames flickering in the hearth.

"Sometimes the mist lifts for a heartbeat. Then we see what is there," Rymi said gently. "It comforts us to call this a dream."

"I thought I was dreaming, coming back with Sula," Ross said. "We met a woman on the track. Her face was lit up like the moon, and there were animals with her, all sorts of animals. She had a basket with loads of berries in. A raven brought me some."

"Did you take any?"

Ross nodded. "I was starving."

Rymi smiled broadly. "All is well then. Now, work. Something I promised Tilda." Beside him lay a small heap of antler pieces that he spread out to assess, before selecting a couple. "You enjoy carving," he murmured, inspecting the two minutely.

"Do I? I don't know." Now I'm going to get told off for the sled, Ross thought. Yet to his surprise Rymi said cheerfully, "See what you make of this."

Ross turned the bit of antler over, and back again. Although he hadn't a clue what to do, he was willing to make an attempt. "I haven't anything to carve with," he said.

Rymi went to search among some bags, and returned with an odd little knife. It had a stubby wooden handle, and a very short blade. He handed it to Ross, saying, "Look into the antler. See what waits within."

Ross examined his bit of antler more carefully. It was branched, like a hand with the fingers squashed together and the thumb held out. When he turned it on its side he saw an open mouth.

"Watch," Rymi said. In the palm of his left hand he held a piece of antler, and in the other hand a knife, gripped like a pen. "Cut a little, not too deep," he said, pressing the tip of the blade forward. "Then turn the antler around, and cut along the line again. Make a groove, like this." He made a V-shape with two fingers. "Now you."

It was difficult to hold the antler steady and cut at the same time, yet Ross managed to create a short, white line. Rymi nodded. "Good. The more you do, the easier it becomes." Satisfied that there would be no severed fingers he pushed his hair behind one ear, and bent over Tilda's amulet.

They worked in silence, each absorbed in his task. But after a while Ross's arms were aching. As he put down the knife his attention was caught by Rymi's's broad belt. Those flying birds and little animals – he must have carved them all himself. Ross took up his star amulet, and looked at it with fresh eyes. It was the best present he had ever had. One day, he promised himself, I'll make something as good as this.

Ross gazed at the original deer-star hanging from a pole, its four hooves bathed in the red glow of the fire. He puzzled over the drum with its mysterious symbols. He admired the copper headdress, the stark animal skull, and the four reindeer antlers set around the hearth. His eyes wandered beyond the circle of firelight, and fell on a pile of reindeer hides. Nestled in the middle was a ball of white fur. It could have been a hat, although one for a very large head. Also, it was breathing.

It's alive!" Ross exclaimed.

At this, the ball of fur opened its eyes. Amber eyes, rimmed with black. They fixed Ross with a predator's stare, blank and unblinking.

Rymi looked up from his engraving. "Lumi often sleeps there," he said, as if it were the most normal thing in the world to have a wolf dozing in his hut. "The others do not know. Best for them, best for him." Ross was thrilled to be so close to a wolf. "I won't tell," he said, eagerly.

Lumi yawned. It was a careless yawn that squeezed his eyelids together and rolled out a pale tongue between gaping jaws. He scrutinised Ross again. Then the wolf rose slightly, shuffled around to lie the other way, and tucked his nose underneath his thick tail. Soon Lumi was back at the lake where fish leapt out, to land helpless at his feet.

Enthused by this encounter, Ross set to work again. The spirit of the wolf would flow in every line.

~

"You are quiet, Tilda. Are you ailing?"

"No, Nanna."

"Don't pretend. I know you too well. Here, let me tidy your hair."

Tilda moved around the fire to sit with her back to her elder-Ma. Hirta worked through the long hair a handful at a time, teasing out tangles with her bone comb. "This is like before," Tilda said wistfully. "If only everything could be like before."

Hirta was glad that Tilda couldn't see her face, because she felt near to tears. She separated three strands, and began to plait. The hair was so like her own, when she was that age. "Tell me what troubles you," Hirta said, in as bright a voice as she could manage.

Tilda sighed. "The trees, Nanna. My head aches with their thoughts."

Hirta stopped plaiting. "Have you spoken to Rymi?"

"He says I will grow used to it. It is a blessing."

"He would say that," Hirta muttered. She had always dreaded that one of the family might be called, always feared that it was in their blood. Why must it be her dear little calf? But the gift often skipped a generation. She finished the plait, binding the end with a length of deer sinew.

"Maybe he is right," Tilda said, turning to face her.

"He is usually, whether for good or ill." Hirta reached out to stroke Tilda's cheek. "Do not fear, little one. Whatever comes, we will make good from it." Then, softly, Hirta began to sing. It was a song of winter's end, of reindeer calves and golden catkins.

~

In the hut they continued engraving, until Rymi put down his work to pour some tea. Ross was pleased with what he'd done. There were only a few mistakes, and nobody would notice because he'd made them look like fur. Emboldened by his newly discovered skill, Ross wondered if this was the moment to ask about the skull. He knew he wasn't supposed to, but it fascinated him. "Did you kill it?" he asked, thrilled by the powerful overlapping canines and the empty eye sockets that seemed to see everything.

Slowly, Rymi took a drink from his tea-stained bowl. "No," he said finally. Ross persisted. "Who did? Was it chasing them?"

"This is not for firelight talk." The blunt words were delivered with a challenging look, Rymi's way of ending unwanted conversations. Ross knew he'd gone too far. He gazed sadly at the pine logs spitting in the fire. Yet, seeing his disappointment, Rymi relented. "When I was very young," he said, "there was a great hunger. Even the wolves were skin and bone – only ravens grew fat. Nobody chose to hunt the sleeper. Our men went to find him so everyone could be fed."

"Is that him?" Ross asked. "The sleeper?"

Rymi nodded. "Hunting him brings danger. Forest-Ma may be angry. We cannot take, unless she is willing to give.

And the sleeper is clever. He hears all we say. If we name him, if we say what he is, he knows we are coming for him. So we call him sleeper, or–"

"Tatterback?"

Rymi smiled grimly. "Names have power."

"Is that why you say soul-binder? You can't say his real name?"

Rymi's smile vanished. He stared into his tea, while Ross wished – oh, how he wished – he could take back that word. Eventually Rymi sighed and said, "You have something else to tell me."

The dream. Ross had almost forgotten. He opened his mouth to speak, but had the oddest feeling that others were there, listening. He glanced over his shoulder.

"Pay no attention to them," Rymi said.

"Them?" Ross could hear his own heart pounding.

"The spirits. They are curious, that is all. They will not hurt you."

"Oh. Right." Ross's eyes roamed the shadowy walls, looking for... What, exactly? "It was the weirdest thing," he said in a low voice. "There was this pool, all green and glowing. I was swimming. Not in water, it was sort of like the Wayfinders."

Soft lights were dappling the wall like restless moonbeams. Ross glanced nervously at Rymi, who nodded at him to continue. "Then something fished me out. I was back in the forest, and a tree turned into a woman, the one with the moon face and the berries."

Ross could see them now, coming closer. They drifted around the fire on ragged wings, filling his ears with their mewing, peering at him with their filmy white eyes. As they hovered nearby the air stirred like breath. He wanted to wave his hands to keep them away, but was afraid that he might touch them.

"Now hear my story," Rymi said. "It was my twelfth summer. Fa sent me to help the one who had killed the sleeper. I saw him treat the sick, find lost deer, lost people. In these ways the healer earned respect. From him I learned the secrets of the drum, how to prepare herbs. I watched as he made amulets."

As he spoke the lights faded, and the mewing ceased. But Ross knew the spirits were still there, listening.

"He looked into my soul," Rymi went on, "and saw I was born for the path. I thought not. Later, when the seeing began, I fought it. When we are young, we do not want to be… different."

"But they're here now, the spirits."

"I tried to keep them away. They came more and more – spirits of fire, of wind, of water."

"So you didn't want them," Ross said. "They sort of chose you."

Rymi laughed, although he looked deadly serious. "The spirits decide."

Ross knew in his heart what this meant. They would help you, but they'd always be in charge. He felt his stomach knot. "I saw the moon-faced woman with the berries," he said, "and your spirit birds."

"You have the gift. Use will hone your skill. Like engraving."

"I don't see your hearth-keeper."

"She rarely shows herself, even to me," Rymi said. "But you saw forest-Ma. All things that live here thrive because of her. Trees, herbs, creatures, reindeer folk – we all hear her voice. We all honour her." He smiled, and the black claws at his throat glinted in the firelight. "You ate her berries. Now you are hers."

"What?"

"This is a fine thing, Ross. She will protect you, after I… when I am not here."

Ross scratched his head. He had so many questions. "The green pool. What was that?" But Rymi, it seemed, had said enough. "You will know soon. Now you must go. To wake Tilda's amulet, I need all my spirits."

Ross got to his feet reluctantly. His mind was whirling, yet he didn't want to leave. He held out the knife.

"It is yours," Rymi said.

"Thanks."

"Keep the blade sharp. Tilda will show you how."

Ross was opening the door when Rymi called out, "How is your eye? Enough ointment?"

"It feels better. That stuff really helps."

"If you need more, be sure to ask."

"I will. Thanks."

"Now go," Rymi said, waving him away. "Tell Tilda to come after breakfast."

~

"What is it?" Hirta asked, squinting at the piece of antler. This wasn't the reaction Ross had hoped for. He sighed heavily. "Can't you tell?"

Tilda got up from the fireside to have a closer look. "I know – a dog, yawning." Hirta nodded in agreement. "Oh, of course. I was looking at it upside down."

"It's a wolf," Ross said, crossly. "And he's howling."

Hirta told him it was very good, for his first one. "When it is finished, I will show you how to colour the lines – wood ash for grey, charcoal for black. You could have red, but boiling alder bark makes a terrible stink." Ross grinned. "Black would be great."

Later he took the little box from his pocket, and pulled off the lid. The ointment was lasting really well. He liked

134

how it felt cool and tingly. He liked it so much that he smoothed some on the other eye as well. Funny, how there never seemed to be any less.

14

The Ice Fall

The glowing sky was crammed with stars as they carried the buckets back from the spring, boots rustling through the powdery snow. Ross walked carefully, trying not to spill the precious water. In front of him Tilda was slowing down, and he guessed that she was touching the amulet around her neck. "Do you like it?" he said.

"Of course. Why do you ask?"

"Well, it's a–"

"Owl?"

Tilda stopped to lower her bucket onto the snow. "See," she said, holding up the amulet, "this is not like *him*. This is a hawk-owl. It turns sorcery back on the sorcerer. No shadow can touch me, Rymi says. Not in the forest, or on the fells, or on the lake."

Ross took in the bold, staring eyes, bristling feathers, and squared-off tail. Something about it made him look away quickly. "It scares me, anyway." He made an owl face, and Tilda laughed. Then her expression clouded. "We should not mock the spirits."

"Suppose not," Ross replied, remembering the host of white-eyed spirit birds. For a moment they exchanged awkward glances. Then Tilda suggested they go to check on the herd. "You can take a sled if you like."

"Bet I get there first," Ross said.

~

Ross made a disappointing start. His reindeer, Lausa, was an unwilling plodder who kept stopping to look back at the camp. Yet when he realised Miri was pressing ahead, Lausa had a swift change of mind. Soon Ross was steering his sled alongside Tilda's. "Not too fast," she called out. "Keep the reins short."

Ross took that as a challenge. Slackening the reins he shouted, "Hoy! Hoy!" Lausa responded. Seeing the other deer passing him, Miri increased his pace to match. Now they had a race. They sped across the ice, one in front, then the other, with the two dogs galloping after them.

~

Hirta came out of the tent to find Rymi preparing firewood. He was on one knee in the snow, chopping branches so they would fit in the hearth. "Should they go off on their own, the way things are?" Hirta asked, watching the sleds racing across the lake. "One of us should be with them."

"Youth is short. Let them enjoy it," he said, glancing at her as he trimmed the twigs off a branch. "Whatever happens, they will know what to do."

"Easy for you to say."

Rymi threw down the branch. "She has my amulet," he said, in a tone sharp as the axe blade. Silently, Hirta cursed her hasty speech. Worry always loosened her tongue, so the wrong words slipped out. "I hardly know what I say," she said, sadly. "That monster's shadow is on my heart." Rymi got to his feet, and leaned the axe against the pile of firewood. "That one wills fear on us all," he muttered, staring at the forest on the far bank.

Hirta watched him from the corner of her eye. It was the same covert method she used with the firesprite, the old way of seeing things that are not quite of this world. She knew her next words must be chosen with care. "This thing, you say you have to do. It must be important, for you to risk so much."

Rymi turned quickly, with an odd expression that she couldn't make out. "Be sure of this," he said, "nothing in this world is more important."

~

"I win," Ross called, halting his reindeer at the edge of the lake.

"Not till you are off the ice."

Ross saw the flash of Miri's white face as Tilda's sled swept past and up the bank. Then a shrub under the snow caught at the runners, dragging her sledge to a slewing stop. Tilda fell off, and rolled in the snow, laughing. "Neither of us won."

After Ross had helped her to free the sled, they tied Miri and Lausa to two trees. The reindeer stood with mouths open, panting, their breath lingering in clouds among the branches. Tilda called the dogs, and looked around expecting to see the herd. No familiar shapes were moving among the trees. She stared at the churned up snow. "Something has frightened them," she said. Ross shrugged. He said they were sure to be around somewhere. "They know," Tilda said, watching Larna and Fann sniff at the disturbed snow. "And the trees know. They are restless. Do you not hear them?"

Ross frowned. The trees were still, and he could hear nothing. Yet as he gazed into the forest, something strange happened. A jag of light flashed inside his head. When he could see again, everything had changed. In front of him

– no more than a breath away – a steep stairway of ice stretched up and up, glassy and vibrantly blue. The vision was so vivid it hurt. Gasping, Ross scrubbed at his eyes. He heard Tilda ask if something was wrong.

"I thought… It's nothing. It's gone now."

"Sure? You look shocked."

Was this what Rymi meant by the seeing? He wanted to ask, but at that moment Fann rushed up, barking. They followed him to a dip where a stream slept under the snow. On the other side a group of reindeer were pulling strands of lichen off a tree trunk. "You found some deer," Tilda said, gripping the dog's ruff and giving him a playful shake. "Good work, Fann."

Larna had stayed at the lakeside, and now she began to bark. Tilda shouted at her to be quiet. The barking began again, more insistently this time.

They found Larna on the bank with ears pricked, her twitching nose pointing down the lake. Following her stare they strained for a movement to disturb the white calm, or a sound to break the silence.

"Did you hear that?"

"What?"

"Listen," Tilda said. "There, the herd bell. Olli is over there."

"Maybe he wanted a change."

"He would never leave the others. Not unless something made him. Come on."

Their sleds skimmed along the lake past white, wooded slopes, and little bays scattered with boulders. Then, led on by the bell, they crossed to the other side. Ahead of them the bank jutted out into the ice, blocking their view, but as they rounded the little headland all became clear.

A bay stretched back to a deep cleft in the cliff, where only a few months ago rushing water had tumbled to the lake. Now winter held the cascade motionless, locked in mid flow. At its foot, a group of reindeer huddled miserably among icy boulders. Sure enough, Olli was with them, his white spectacles showing plainly in the twilight. They took the sleds as close as they could, and stared up at the frozen waterfall.

Ross was stunned. This was his vision – ice steps of intense blue. Near the top, stunted birches clung to the rocks on either side. And up there, among the branches, he saw the gleam of the herd bell.

"*He* did this," Tilda whispered, touching her hawk-owl amulet.

They glanced around furtively, hearts thumping. Every strange boulder or wind-twisted tree became suspect. "He could be anywhere," Ross said. "Or anything," Tilda replied. There were clumps of twigs on the steep banks, and saplings among the rocks, but among them the blue-tinted snow lay undisturbed. In the bare branches, nothing stirred.

"Perhaps he has gone," Tilda said hopefully, although neither of them quite believed it. "We must get the reindeer back to the herd. Look, they are terrified." They tethered their sled deer, and then moved towards the others, slowly so as not to cause more alarm. As they approached, Olli and the cows closed up to hide the calves. The reindeer knew Tilda well, yet they remained highly stressed, showing the whites of their eyes.

Ross and Tilda spread their arms wide to shoo the deer away from the bottom of the cliff. At first this seemed likely to work, until the frightened animals turned as one and rushed back towards the bell. Quickly the dogs cut in front, but the reindeer ignored them. Once more they clustered at the base of the fall, too afraid even to make a sound.

"They think they are safe near the herd bell. They will never come away till we stop it ringing," Tilda said, removing her lasso. She made a good throw, but instead of catching the bell, the loop fell around a rock. Ross watched as she tugged on the lasso, leaning back with all her weight. "Caught fast," she sighed, resigned to losing it.

"Suppose I'll have to go up and get it," Ross said.

"Too dangerous. That ice hanging over, it could shatter in the blink of an eye."

Ross knew she was right. Thick swags fringed with icicles hung from every boulder. Further down these merged into a single sheet that splayed across the ground. It would be impossible to climb. But down the edge where the lasso dangled, fingers of ice crept between dark rocks, leaving narrow ledges that looked like possible footholds.

"I can get up there, at the side."

"Maybe," Tilda said, doubtfully. "You could tie the lasso around your waist. Then you will not fall so far."

"Oh, thanks."

Ross picked his way among ice-covered boulders to the edge of the fall. He tucked the star underneath his sweat top and began to climb. The first bit was not too difficult, which was just as well, because when he slipped he could recover easily. But as the cliff began to rise more steeply he had to stop, and pass the line around his waist. This wasn't easy to do without pushing himself off the narrow ledge. Fumbling with the line, he remembered when Grandad showed him how to tie knots. If only he had paid more attention.

Ross moved more slowly, searching for handholds with his mittens, feeling for ledges with his soft-soled boots. Breathing harder, he stopped for a moment, pressing his cheek against the freezing rock. He'd almost reached the place where a deep shelf ran behind the curtain of ice. He squinted upwards into the dark space. A face peered back.

Horrified, Ross gasped, flattening his body against the rock. Fluffy white fur, slanted eyes, black button nose –a fox. For a few, breathless seconds he stared into its eyes. The fox showed its pointy teeth, and Ross heard, "Back, back." Then the animal turned, and with a swish of its white brush it was gone.

Sweat rolled down his neck. Maybe he ought to go back.

Don't be stupid, Ross told himself, you're nearly there. Foxes bark. That's all it was. Scrabbling clumsily, he hauled himself onto the wide shelf. Icicles skittered off to shatter on the rocks below. He heard Tilda shout, are you all right? But he couldn't reply. He knelt, gasping for breath. No sign of the fox. It must have gone behind the frozen waterfall.

When Ross looked up the bell was close. He reached out a hand to catch its strap. That seemed to be a signal for everything to happen – the dogs started barking, Tilda shouted, and something went rushing across the cliff above, sending loose snow down onto his head. He glanced across, and saw them on the headland, ghosts against the dark sky.

"Wolves!" Tilda shouted.

"I'm coming down," Ross shouted back.

He tugged on the strap. The bell sprang off the sapling, clonking. Ross knelt on the shelf, hugging the bell close. He wasn't sure about going down. He could abseil, using the lasso. That would be the fastest way, except that he didn't know how. The only thing was to keep on climbing. It wasn't far to the top. And if he did that, Tilda could have her lasso back.

Ross hung Olli's bell around his neck. Although his fingers were clumsy inside the mittens, he managed to loosen the lasso, and ease it from around the rock. He wound the line into hasty loops, looking around for something to weight it. A broken icicle would have to do. A quick glance down showed the reindeer near the bottom of the cliff, with the girl and the dogs in front of them.

"Tilda! Got the lasso. I'm throwing it. Now."

Using the sapling to steady himself, Ross flung the lasso as far out as he could. He didn't watch it fall. But he heard the icicle smash into bits.

Going up was easier now. The slope was less steep, and offered more handholds. As he climbed Ross puzzled over the vision – he'd seen something before it happened. Why? Was it saying you have to do this, but don't worry everything will come right? Or perhaps it was some kind of warning.

The sound of the bell was so annoying he wondered how Olli could put up with it. As he paused to shove the bell inside his coat, hoping that would muffle it, a niggling thought struck him. None of the trees were moving. There wasn't even a whisper of wind. Yet when the bell was caught on the rock, something had made it ring.

Suddenly there was no more up. Scrambling over the last rock, Ross heaved himself over the edge, and lay face down in the snow. His arms burned, and his legs were jellybeans, but he didn't care. He'd made it. Yet the relief was short lived. As he raised his head he saw, a hand's length from the end of his nose, a huge paw print.

The back of the print was smudged where the paw had slid into the snow. But the four toes with thick claws were all too horribly distinct. As they dug in, they had pushed up a little crescent of snow. He hadn't thought of it before, but now Ross realised that to reach the lake, he'd have to take the same route as the wolves. Maybe they'd be waiting for him.

"Where've you been, Ross, I've been looking all over."

"GRANDAD!"

Ross leapt to his feet, delirious with joy. It was him it was! There was Grandad seated on a boulder, in his weird jumper and shapeless old trousers. Ross saw nothing else. He forgot Tilda, the wolves, even where he was. Hurtling forward he slipped on the snow-covered ice, put down a hand to steady himself, then ran headlong. His only thought was to hug his grandfather.

Grandad was close. His hands reached out. Ross threw his arms wide, but as he did, the star sent a scorching pain across his chest. He slid to a halt, doubled over, gasping. The enchantment lifted, and it all flooded back, what had happened to Grandad. That couldn't be him. What he was seeing wasn't real. Reality was the frozen pool under his feet, the hillside hung with icicles, and spattered with snow. Yet it was still there, the unreal thing. It was close enough to touch. Not that he wanted to – he'd rather the wolves ate him.

Even though he felt revolted, Ross couldn't help but stare. The shell of skin and clothes was concealing something, it wasn't hard to guess what. He knew who was peering through Grandad's eyes.

"Aw, did you miss me?" Grandad's lips moved, although the voice was his no longer. "I took a little trip. Guess where."

Don't care, Ross thought, his mouth too dry to speak. He felt empty, hollowed out.

"She will care, your friend the birch girl."

That stung. The sorcerer was stealing his thoughts – that was how he'd shaped this cruel illusion, this image of his dear, dead Grandad.

"At the settlement, that's where I was. Nobody saw me. All they saw was a harmless old owl."

Tilda's family... Ross didn't want to think, it was too

awful. He wanted to sink into the snow and curl up. Then he thought, the soul-binder knows that, too.

"I liked it there," the voice continued. "So many souls, all in one place. So much choice, I hardly knew where to begin."

Suddenly the star was a white-hot brand, shocking Ross from his lethargy. From the corner of his eye he saw the neck of land curving into the lake. He balled his hands into fists. Stepped backwards.

But quick as he was, the sorcerer was quicker. A hand flashed out to seize him by the wrist. Ross cried out in panic, "No! The star–"

The soul-binder laughed. His grip was glacier cold, the force enough to snap bone. The Grandad mask, with the sorcerer's hellish eyes, came right up to Ross's face. "Your souls are mine now," he whispered.

Ross shrank from the bleak, empty eyes, from the spinning force that was drawing him in. His head swam. He felt sick. The ghastly face turned grey, then faded to nothing. Ross felt his body slip away, taking with it every sensation. He couldn't see or hear, smell or feel. He was alone, tiny, suspended in darkness.

For a few terrifying seconds Ross was very afraid. But all at once his body came back, and he found himself dangling in mid-air. Confused, gasping for breath, he felt the chilling hand let go of his wrist. As he flopped onto the ice he heard that mocking voice again, "What are you doing down there? Get up."

The ice was hard as steel. Ross lay face down, trying to work out if he could feel anything. The herd bell was digging into his shoulder. His heart was beating so fast it hurt.

"I said, get up." A blow to his ribs sent Ross sliding into a rock, yet the sorcerer continued to torment him. "I have

words for your master," he said. "You will deliver them."
Fearing another kick, Ross dragged himself up to lean on
the rock. He waited for his instructions. Instead the sorcerer
growled, "Want me to change my mind? RUN."

Ross ran. Scuttling like a vole, fleeing like prey, his mind
was a mash of terror and despair. Grandad's cheery voice
floated after him. "Remember me to Rymi. Tell the old fool
I'll see him soon."

Ross wanted to yell and scream. But he knew that if he
did, he would shatter into pieces. He ran blindly, wallowing
in deep snow, sliding over rocks, until one foot slipped and
flew up in the air. Snow smacked him on the back. The
bell dinned in his ears. Stars went shooting past, faster and
faster. Waving his arms helplessly, he shot over the edge of
the cliff.

15

A Sacrifice

Tilda had seen the white fox. So she wasn't surprised to hear voices at the top of the frozen waterfall. Although she couldn't make out the words, she knew all too well what Ross had found. Then came the clashing of the bell, the crashing and wrenching of branches. Something was rolling down the slope, among the birches.

But in spite of this new threat, she had to concentrate on the wolves. She'd lost sight of them among the haze of birches – they must have gone down another way. Six, she'd counted. They would cause confusion, try to separate the calves. Tilda grasped the strikestone and chopped at the steel again. Fire was the only thing that would keep them away.

A hot spark hit the tinder. She cupped the shredded fungus in her bare hands, blowing until it flamed. Beside her Larna growled, a deep, chesty rumble, and suddenly the wolves were there, at the end of the headland. Quickly Tilda transferred the flame to the twiggy branch. The pine popped and crackled, flaring suddenly against the dark sky. She had a weapon.

The wolves spread out, blocking the way onto the lake. They were not like Lumi, well fed with dried fish, but scrawny, even in their winter coats. She almost pitied them. Two of them sat down to watch her. They looked old and in no hurry. Keeping her eyes on the wolves, Tilda replaced the fire-making kit in its pouch. She had passed the lasso through the dogs' neckbands, and held it fast under her boot – now the dogs were straining against it. Fann's mane was bristling, while along Larna's back the hair was stiff as spruce needles. Both were barking. Tilda gave the lasso a sharp tug. She couldn't afford to risk her dogs in a fight.

Meanwhile, the pack had split up. The old wolves stayed behind to cut off any escape, while the others slipped among the rocks, heading towards the reindeer. Gripping the spitting torch in the crook of one arm, Tilda pulled on her mittens. Then she grabbed the improvised leash, and held the torch aloft. She was ready. Behind her, Olli and the cows began to circle. They moved as one, heads up, breath hanging in a single cloud. Instinct told them to run, yet the bell called on them to stay.

Nearby, Miri and Lausa tugged at their tethers, desperate to escape. Their lines had been secured in the usual way, easy for cold fingers to release. Don't work loose now, she thought, it's a long walk back to camp. But what if the wolves turned on Miri, tied up and helpless? Would the torch be enough to stop them?

The wolves kept coming. There was nonchalance in their easy, long-legged trot, with tongues lolling from jaws, tails held straight out behind. They were close enough for their eyes to shine in the torchlight. Tilda swung the fiery branch from side to side, making arcs of smoke and light. The wolves gave the flames a wary glance, and moved further away. But it was obvious they weren't afraid of her, or the dogs.

Behind her the circling stopped. The reindeer took off. The wolves shot across in front of her, bounding after the deer, while the dogs threw themselves against her legs, almost pushing her over.

Tilda knew that reindeer could outrun wolves. Olli and the cows had a chance to get away, if they could slip past the pair on the lakeside. But one of the youngsters was struggling to keep up. The leading wolf was closing on it. She saw the calf trip. Her heart stood still. The calf recovered, and ran on, but the wolf was close enough to snap at its tail.

Then something remarkable happened. Olli swung out from among the racing cows, and stopped dead. Bracing his front legs, he lowered his head into the path of the onrushing wolf.

As the calf skipped past Olli, the wolf saw its fate. Its claws scrabbled wildly at the ice, yet it couldn't stop itself from sliding onto the antlers. With a flick of his head Olli scooped up the wolf, and tossed it into the air. It landed on a rock with a yelp, and didn't move.

Olli turned to run, but he had left it too late. The other three were on him.

Tilda watched helplessly as the horror unfolded. One wolf caught him by a hind leg, another by the tail. Olli staggered a few steps, trying to kick them off, until the third wolf seized him at the shoulder. Old Olli stumbled and went down in a haze of snow and thrashing hooves. When they saw that, the old wolves abandoned their post. Ignoring the cows and calves, the pair came running to share in the kill. The remaining reindeer, seizing their chance, fled across the lake.

Maddened by the blood and the ghastly sounds, the two sled deer leapt wildly on their tethers. Tilda hurried towards them, checking them over as she ran. Nothing too wrong, just a rein wrapped around Lausa's front leg. And Miri's single antler lay on the ice, cast off as he struggled to be free.

Tilda couldn't handle two frantic deer. Jamming the torch between some rocks, she untied Lausa and let him go, sled and all. Larna yipped as the fleeing sled ran over her paw, and in her haste to help the dog, Tilda tripped over the fallen antler. Still on her knees she freed Miri's rein, hanging on somehow as he plunged and pranced. "Steady, Miri. Calm down." Not much hope of that. Tilda heard fear in her voice, and she knew that he could hear it too.

~

Ross rolled down the slope in a blizzard of powder. Snow filled his ears, his mouth, his hood, and poured down the neck of his coat. The bell rang as if it would never be stopped. Branches rapped his face as he crashed from one bendy birch to another, tumbling faster and further, until a boulder stopped his headlong rush. Cradled between snow, twigs and rock he lay burning up, his blood pounding. He'd done it. Got away.

He wasn't totally safe, though. Ross was almost upside-down at the edge of a drop, staring into the blue-black sky. A crowd of stars stared back at him. After what he'd seen, they looked so clean and pure. He blinked. Among the stars was a slender crescent moon. Ross remembered Rymi's promise. It couldn't be time, not yet. He wasn't ready.

Once again he was shifting, slipping. The fur cap came off, and rolled away. Groping for a hold, Ross closed his mitten around a root. It cracked, and tore away. Still holding the treacherous root, he slid around the boulder on a raft of loose twigs, and fell into nothing.

The landing left Ross breathless. Yet he didn't feel any worse, except that his ears stung from the cold, and his head ached. He felt for the phone. By some miracle it was still in his pocket. He kept his eyes closed. Everything felt better that way.

Suddenly Tilda was tugging at his arm. "Nothing broken," she said, jamming the fur cap onto his head. "You fell in a snowdrift." Ross groaned. The cap, lined with snow, was numbing his brain. He squinted at her stupidly as she lurched to one side shouting, "Miri! Stop! On the sled, quick – he is going without us." Ross slithered off the heap of snow, and crawled onto the sled. Parts of him were beginning to complain. "Hold tight," Tilda ordered, "or be thrown off."

~

Hirta pulled open the door of the hut.

"Rymi?"

The fire had burned so low that at first she saw nothing. As she hesitated in the doorway the draught roused some weak flames, enough to see the bare soles of his feet. Rymi was lying, flat out, near the hearth. For an awful moment she thought he was gone. Then a toe twitched, and Hirta breathed again. He had drifted off while warming his feet at the fire.

She stepped inside, glancing around in case of spirits. It did not feel right to come in without asking. Cautiously she approached the sleeping figure, and bent over him, speaking in a very loud whisper, "Rymi! Wake up! Something bad has happened." His eyes opened so suddenly that she flinched. "The lad's reindeer is back. On its own."

Rymi raised himself on one elbow, yawning and rubbing his neck. "What? Nothing has happened, Hirta. I would have seen."

This was true. The firesprite had given no warning either. Perhaps she was worrying too much. "I know, but the deer is in a state. And I heard a wolf." At this Rymi sat up, and began pulling on his boots. His eyes searched the shadows, but the one he looked for was not there. "Maybe it was Lumi you heard."

They hurried outside to find a wretched-looking reindeer with a battered sled. Rymi took Lausa's head in both hands, and looked into the frightened eyes. "What is it?" Hirta asked. What happened?"

"Wolves."

This was good news, in one sense. Wolves, she could understand. Hirta unfastened Lausa from the sled and led him away to tether him with the others, before rushing back to join Rymi at the lakeside.

The Wayfinders were sweeping the sky with their torches, flooding the expanse of ice with green and yellow. So powerful were the Lights, that Hirta felt sure she could hear them. A kind of rustling, it was. Their uncanny force was at work on Rymi's hair, fluffing it into hares' tails.

After the green came a flood of red. Hirta shivered – that always made her think of blood. Then she saw the sled in the distance, a dull blur under the shifting red light. It was moving erratically, weaving from side to side. There seemed to be only one person on it. Shading her gaze with a hand, Hirta narrowed her eyes. Was that Miri? The reindeer had no antlers, but that was his white blaze, she was certain, and yes, that was Tilda driving. The lad was behind her. He looked hurt. Her heart lifted to see the dogs, although it sank again at the sight of Larna limping.

"Bring them into the hut," Rymi called, already walking away. "I will build up the fire."

~

Tilda had strained a shoulder while tussling with Miri. Ross ached, and his bruises were sore, yet luckily there was nothing serious. They sat before the hearth watching the flames leap and crackle, sipping reluctantly from their bowls of hot tea. Rymi had stirred in a powdered herb, assuring them that it would soothe their aches, but it made the drink unpleasantly bitter.

Ross felt chilled, even though he was wrapped in a reindeer skin. His top, damp with sweat and melted snow, lay drying beside him. He stared blankly at the wisps of vapour rising from the fabric, leaving Tilda to explain what had happened. Talk, he could do without.

In a flat voice she told how they came to be in the bay, and how Ross scaled the waterfall to retrieve the herd bell. But when it came to the wolves and Olli, Tilda faltered. What she saw in her mind was too painful to put into words. "Anyway," she mumbled, turning the bowl between her hands, "the cows got away."

"Never mind. Tell us later," Hirta said gently. "Now drink your tea. That spring water makes a good brew."

Rymi was examining Larna's injury. As he held her paw she gazed at him with sorrowful eyes, and tried to lick his face. The cut to her pad was deep. Yet she made no fuss when he cleaned it, or when he rubbed in healing balm. Once the ordeal was over Rymi offered her half a dried fish, which Larna took politely. Holding her damaged pad clear of the floor she hopped away to chew her treat in the shadows. Rymi took his knife, sliced a leg from the deerskin he was sitting on, and began to fashion a little boot to protect the dog's paw.

"At least we still have reindeer luck," Hirta said, attempting to lift her own spirits as well as theirs. "Things could be worse."

"No," Tilda said, in a sudden outburst. "Things are worse. The sorcerer was there, with some wolves. It was all his doing. Olli is dead, Nanna. The wolves killed him."

Hirta listened, stony faced, as Tilda described how Olli killed the wolf, saved the calf, and allowed the others to escape. "No need to feel bad, little one. There was nothing you could do," Hirta said, in a low voice. "Always had his own mind, did Olli. Never one to do what you expect." She wasn't usually sentimental about reindeer, but... She wiped the back of her hand across one eye. "I was going to keep his antlers, to put on my grave."

"Oh, Nanna." Tilda reached out to take her hand, but Hirta did not notice. She hadn't finished yet. "Is this our fate, to be prey for wolves and demons? If we lose our herd, we are ruined. And you," she turned on Rymi, "how could you? You watched them go. You must have known that monster was out there, you must have."

This was no way to speak to a friend, especially one who sees. Tilda and Ross exchanged furtive glances, and kept their heads down. Yet Rymi didn't react to Hirta's tirade. He stared at the needle pushed halfway through the deerskin, as still as an old guardian carved from wood.

"I did not see."

"What do you mean," Hirta said, with a tremor in her voice. "Of course you did."

"I tell you, I saw nothing."

The colour drained from Hirta's face. Had he lost the help of his spirits? No, that wasn't it. And then she knew, with terrible clarity. The sorcerer had become stronger – stronger than Rymi.

For a while, each of them hugged their own sadness. Then all at once Rymi began to sing. Or rather, hum. The low, tuneless drone was not meant for human ears, and it did nothing to ease their misery.

Ross was thinking about poor Olli. He hadn't known what the wolves had done because he'd been too dazed to notice, what with falling down the cliff and everything. It was sad to think he wouldn't see Olli again, with his funny face and stubborn ways. But at least the wolves hadn't got Miri.

The welt on his chest was stinging. Ross ran his fingers over the raised, red skin, tracing the shape of the amulet. It felt like nettle rash, only worse. Oddly, he didn't mind, even though the star hadn't stopped the soul-binder's attack. But his wrist was another matter. The sorcerer's grip had left a white band all the way around. Certain it was frostbite, Ross had asked if his hand would drop off, yet Rymi had said no, it was only frost-nip. Warm it gently, he advised, not too close to the fire – in the armpit is best. So, with a sigh, Ross tucked his wrist back under the opposite arm.

Rymi was still humming, intensifying the awkward mood in the hut. Ross didn't want to interrupt yet he had to tell him what the sorcerer said. He scratched his head. That bit about the settlement – should he mention that? Perhaps it wasn't true. Maybe it was just talk, meant to hurt. He hoped so, anyway. "I've got a message from *him*. From the soul-binder," he said.

The humming stopped abruptly. Ross plunged into the silence. " 'Remember me to Rymi, tell the old fool I'll see him soon.' That was it. Sorry. That's what he said."

A faint, sad smile twitched one corner of Rymi's mouth. He looked at least a hundred years old.

"How has it come to this?" Hirta demanded. "Why not stop him before, when he was weaker?"

Rymi made no reply. He resumed work on Larna's paw guard, apparently absorbed in the stitching, while Hirta struggled to contain her anger. But as she watched him, she felt guilt for her words. How could he risk taking on the sorcerer? Rymi had not passed on the craft. If he died now, his souls could never reach the upperworld, never help the living. They would be blown like snow, and all his knowledge gone forever. There was only one thing to be done. "We should go to the nameless stones," Hirta said. "Sacrifice to the Old Ones. A life, for our lives."

The fire brightened. The air crackled with tension. Ross saw the pale birds gathering around Rymi, stroking his hair with their tattered wings. He glanced at the others. They could not see the spirits as he did. "Hirta's right," Ross said, from beneath his reindeer skin. "There's got to be a way. We can't give up."

While he was speaking the spirit birds drifted over to him. They hovered around his head uttering forlorn cries, trailing streamers of torn spider silk. The sound was the saddest that Ross had ever heard, a song of lonely winds, and the shadows of passing clouds. He found himself blinking back painful memories. Then the whole hurtful story flooded out, how much he missed his grandfather, and how the sorcerer had used this to deceive him.

The others listened in silence. At the end Ross rubbed his eyes, sore from unshed tears. He reached into his pocket for Rymi's green ointment. It slid across his burning lids, cool and silky as moss.

When Ross opened his eyes, the seeing was happening again. Where the fire had been was a wash of blue-green, sky in water, water in sky. Through it flew a white bird, a lone tundra swan, its neck stretched out, and feet tucked up behind. As he gazed at the swan, a glutinous sludge bubbled up. It oozed over the bird, smothering its wing-beats, sucking at its feathers. The swan was being dragged to its doom. Yet the powerful wings beat hard, shaking off the cloying mess. The swan ran across the sky-water, lifted off, and flew strongly as before, with a straggle of other swans following in its wake. Then abruptly the vision was gone.

Although Ross was new to the seeing, already he had a feeling it wasn't always what it seemed. Yet he was certain about the swan. That could mean only one thing. He lifted his head, and met Rymi's eyes.

"He'll go on and on stealing souls, you know he will. That's what he's like. He'll come after you and kill you and everything will fall apart. But it doesn't have to be like that," Ross said defiantly. "We won't let it happen. We're going to stop him, before he does any more damage. Then everything will be alright."

Truly, it was a rallying speech. Hirta and Tilda, who'd been ready to comfort him, stared in astonishment at this sudden change. Ross was euphoric. His head buzzed with excitement. Above him the spirit birds tumbled and swooped, and this time he didn't want to shoo them away.

Rymi studied Ross for several moments. He listened to the spirits, twittering joyously. Finally he leaned across to Hirta. "Fate overtakes me," he said, passing her the paw guard, "but the work is almost finished."

Hirta glanced at the little boot. It was complete, perfect – that was not what he meant. With a sinking heart she asked what he was going to do, but her words hung unanswered in the air.

Rymi got up from the fire, and went over to his seer's coat. For a while he stood deep in thought, gazing at the white reindeer hair. Suddenly, he bent to pick it up. As he eased it over his shoulders the coat came alive with chattering amulets, the muttering of spirit voices. The leather cap he placed on his head, and over it the circlet that sprouted copper antlers.

When he turned to face them he was transformed. Gone was the conflicted, careworn figure. Rymi stood tall, his expression purposeful. He murmured something to his hearth-keeper, causing the fire to flare up among the logs, then strode back to the hearth to stand before the flames. Their red and gold flowed up his white coat, burnishing the amulets, blazing along the antlers. A shadow curved up the wall behind, a shadow that was both man and reindeer.

While the others shrank from the sudden heat, Rymi gazed at them calmly across the flames. "Remember my words – whatever happens, whatever you see, you must not interfere."

Rymi reached into the coat's inside pocket. He brought out a long, thin parcel swathed in soft leather, and began to unwrap it. Hirta and Tilda were puzzled – only Ross knew what that wrapping concealed. As the hare's skin peeled away from the black-barred feather, the spirits shrieked like hawks.

Hirta pleaded, no, not that, but already Rymi was beyond her reach. Holding the feather at arm's length above the flames, he released it into the smoke. For an instant the hot air bore it up. Then, with a tiny flame leaping from every quivering filament, the owl's feather plunged into the heart of the fire.

16

The Old Ones' Spring

Rymi dropped to his knees beside the hearth, heart racing like a reindeer herd running. No time for the drum to slow his pulse. No need, anyway. Focussing all his will, he slowed his heart – beat by beat, beat by beat – until it matched the heartbeat of the Earth.

When his reindeer-spirit came to cast the spell of calm, an eerie stillness stole through the hut. The hearth-fire dwindled to a flicker. The spirit birds stopped in mid-flight, fading into silence. Sensing an approaching storm, the others huddled together.

"What will happen?" Tilda whispered.

"Who knows?" Hirta replied. "Something terrible."

"Maybe we should leave."

"You heard Rymi. He said do nothing."

From far away came an anguished bellow, raw and elemental. Not animal. Not human. There it was again, angrier this time. Then silence.

Larna and Fann came seeking reassurance. Hirta held the dogs close, to whisper calming words. Yet Ross was unafraid. He had seen the swan vision, and was impatient to know what would happen next. The answer came in a distant roar. "I can't just sit here," he said, throwing off the reindeer skin, and pulling on his top. "Me neither," Tilda said, reaching for her coat.

"Sit down, both of you." But even as Hirta spoke, she knew that it was useless. Reluctantly she got to her feet, casting anxious glances at Rymi. Already one soul was in another place, the other still in his kneeling body. The trance was deep. His head drooped, and smoke from the dying fire was curling around the copper antlers. Who knew what terrors he faced? Even if he survived, his soul might need help to return. But the young folk were ready to go, their coats fastened, faces tense with excitement. Who was in the most danger? Hirta hesitated, torn in two. Whatever she did would be wrong.

"Rymi should not do this alone," she said. "You two go, if you must. But stay together. And stay hidden." She hugged them both, saying, "May the Old Ones keep you from harm. May they keep us all." Then, wearied by the endless worry, she turned away to take hold of Larna. With care she lifted the damaged paw, slid it into the little boot, and fastened the ties around the dog's leg. This at least, Hirta hoped, would have a happy outcome. She touched her bear's tooth amulet, just in case.

Tilda and Ross were at the door. "Slowly," Tilda whispered, as they pulled it open, "that will do." The gap was less than a hand's breadth. Narrowing their eyes against the rush of cold air, they saw the Wayfinders' rays go sweeping across the ice. Nothing else was moving. Whatever had made the sound was somewhere out of sight. With a last glance at Hirta, they slipped out of the hut.

Together they ran to the wood stack where pine branches and birch trunks stood upright in a circle, their tops leaning together like tent poles. Tilda moved some trunks aside and crawled in, then Ross pulled the wood back into place behind them. Comfortable, it was not. Twigs filled what little headroom there was, forcing them to crouch, although slits between the trunks allowed a view of camp and lake.

The Lights drifted lazily with stars gleaming through the veils of colour. Stillness lay on the icebound lake, on hazy forest and blue-tinted fell, on every pebble and frozen twig. Yet this stillness was deceptive. The land was not sleeping. From the forest spirit to the smallest gods of spring and hollow, from the vole in its burrow to the bear in her den, every creature felt the threat, and trembled.

Only one dared to shatter the silence. The wolf call soared, died away, then rose and fell again. Tilda sensed triumph in that song, yet no wolves raised their voices in answer. She was wondering where the pack had gone, when Ross's elbow nudged her arm. A shadow was moving down the lake where no shadow should be. It halted opposite the camp, looping and twisting like a swarm of angry insects, before settling into something familiar.

"It's Rymi's apprentice," Ross whispered.

"For now," Tilda muttered.

The figure of Kelvan looked harmless in his habitual grey coat. But what was within quickly grew bored. Wings erupted from the apprentice's back. The coat shrivelled to a fist, and vanished. Hovering above the ice was the demonic form of the sorcerer, seething with fury. Suddenly the wood stack did not seem a wise choice.

"You summoned me, old man. So where are you?" Dark wings raked the sky. Vicious eyes darted slyly from side to side, surveying the camp. "I see your two crows, Rymi, eager to give up their souls."

In the wood stack the young crows cringed. They had picked a stupid place. Become birds in a cage. They could only listen, helpless, to the sinister whistling that grew louder by the second. Overhead a thud, as the arrow struck. Then came the rustling and snapping of twigs. The stack was on fire.

Sparks rained down, singeing their hair. They pulled up their hoods, coughing from the smoke. Where had they come in? It was impossible to tell. The encircling firewood had become a forest, the smoke a mist creeping among the trees. Trunks and branches stretched away, multiplied to infinity as if reflected in a circle of mirrors.

Ross and Tilda knew this was a trick. Yet still they hesitated, held fast by the illusion. As the mist grew denser, increasing their confusion, there was an ominous crunch. "It's collapsing!" Ross shouted. "No," Tilda told him, "Look again."

A gash had appeared in the phantom forest, which widened quickly as another trunk was wrenched away. Instantly, the illusion was banished. Everything was firewood again. Hurling themselves at the gap, they knocked the trunks aside, and rolled in the snow to douse their smouldering deerskins.

They got to their feet, rubbing sore, gritty eyes. Through a film of tears came the blurry shape of a wolf, watching them. At that moment the wood stack flared, and the flames revealed a terrible sight – Rymi's wolf red from muzzle to eyes, his chest smeared with gore. Lumi bared his teeth in a bloodstained grin. By now the stack was well alight, a crackling bonfire pouring smoke into the sky. The noise brought Hirta running, calling on the Old Ones. Then she saw the wolf.

"Lumi saved us," Tilda said quickly. "He dragged the wood away. Helped us get out."

They all stared at the wolf, at the dark, clotted mats on his white chest. No one thought the blood was his. He didn't look hurt, had no injuries that they could see. Hirta feared the blood was Olli's. Tilda assumed it belonged to one of Olli's killers. For Ross there was only one possible explanation – Lumi had fought the whole wolf pack, and beat them.

Meanwhile the wolf had noticed something. The hut door was not properly closed. Lumi trotted straight to it, clawed it open, and slipped inside. Larna's barking began at once. Fearing for her dogs, Hirta started after the wolf, but Tilda caught her arm. "Leave him Nanna. He wants to be with Rymi."

All this time the dreadful presence was hovering over the lake. Hirta glimpsed it now, at the edge of her vision. With a shaking hand she made the sign against evil. Then throwing her arms around Tilda and Ross she hurried them towards the hut, now curiously silent.

They were almost at the door when they saw Lys, the white reindeer. He appeared above the trees, head lifted, listening to the song of the stars. In the curve of his antlers the Lights flowed, green and silver. Rymi's reindeer spirit floated towards them, over the tops of spruce and pine, like drifting snow against the winter night.

The three were transfixed. For a moment they even forgot the sorcerer, so his ugly laugh came as a slap in the face. "Is that it?" he sneered. "An animal spirit?"

Lys was silent, merely shaking his antlers. "Why doesn't he answer," Ross asked, bristling at the insult.

Tilda explained that was not possible. "If he speaks, the sorcerer is freed from the challenge."

Drawing courage from the presence of Rymi's soul kin, they dared to face the lake. For a few moments nothing happened. Then the sorcerer raised a fist, and plunged it into his own chest. They gaped as he wrenched out his heart – or rather, a mouldy lump that might once have been a heart – holding it aloft like a ghastly trophy. A purplish liquid ran through his fingers to splash off the ice, freezing instantly in an arc of spikes. The sorcerer swooped to gather it up, and flung it at Lys.

The three ducked as the bloody icicles hissed over their heads, but the reindeer spirit leapt high so the ice-spikes passed beneath. Lys flew at the sorcerer, who shrank into a grey owl, gliding just out of reach.

Now Lys was on the lake. The owl became a prowling wolf, circling the reindeer spirit, watching for a chance to nip and tear. But Lys anticipated every move. As the wolf slunk around again Lys reared up, and drove his front hooves down onto the wolf's skull.

In the blink of an eye the wolf was a lemming. The hooves missed their target, slammed through the ice, and for a split second the reindeer spirit seemed trapped. Instantly the lemming was gone, replaced by a wolverine slashing at Lys's throat. But the cruel teeth clashed on air – already Lys had slipped free.

With hunched back the wolverine crouched, muscles coiled for another attack. As it sprang, its black hairs were the feathers of a sea eagle flying at Lys's head. Gripping the antlers in its talons the eagle steadied itself with outstretched wings, while the hooked beak reached down to rip out an eye.

Lys whipped his head around, battering the eagle between his antlers. The swirling black feathers became a tangle of twigs, flaming twigs, wedged fast. Trailing burning fragments, the reindeer spirit ran to drive his antlers into a snowdrift. A mist of powdery snow hid the two from sight. When it settled, both had vanished.

The watchers began to breathe again. They looked in every direction, yet there was no sign of the adversaries. "Is it over?" Tilda asked. Ross wanted to know who'd won, but Hirta shook her head. "Only they know."

Suddenly they heard a muffled rumble, like fir trees shrugging off snow. The fighters were back. And this time there was nothing to distinguish one from the other.

Out on the lake stood a white reindeer. Facing him was an identical white reindeer.

They rushed together with lowered heads, antlers meshing in eerie silence. They separated, retreated, charged again. With antlers locked they struggled over the ice, pulling and pushing, sliding and spinning, before spiralling up towards the stars. There the silent battle continued while the Wayfinders' torches, echoing the struggle, swayed back and forth across the sky.

Ross and the herders gazed up in bewilderment. It was impossible to know which was Rymi's soul kin, and which was the shape-shifting sorcerer.

"If his soul kin dies, then Rymi will too," Tilda said, roughly wiping a tear before it could freeze.

"He won't," Ross said confidently. "Rymi will win. I've seen it."

Hirta gave him a sharp look. "I knew it," she muttered, "you used that scrystone." Tilda asked why he had kept his skill hidden, but Ross protested he hadn't. "After our race, when we looked for the herd, that was the first time. I saw the icefall, but I didn't know what it meant." He flinched as Hirta grasped his shoulders, turning him to face her. "Rymi's fate," she demanded, "tell me what you saw. All of it."

"A swan," Ross replied, trying to twist from her grip. "Stuck in mud, going to drown. It got free, and flew away."

Instantly Hirta let go of him, horrified. "A swan? No, no, that–"

The rest was never spoken. Something came tumbling down, turning to vapour before it reached the ice. They looked up in time to see the two white reindeer drawing apart. One had a broken antler.

Now the other had the advantage. He lunged, raking an antler along his foe's undefended side. A gash opened from shoulder to flank, spilling luminous matter into the air. The injured deer spirit drifted away, to drop among the trees somewhere behind the hut.

They turned back towards the lake, hardly daring to look. The other reindeer spirit floated among the stars, looking pure as new snow falling on the high fells. That had to be Rymi's soul kin. Had to be. Grinning wildly they hugged each other, overcome with joy and relief. Ross even let Hirta kiss him, before she hurried back to the hut.

Then Ross and Tilda ran, and leapt, and threw snow at each other, while the victorious spirit watched. They joined hands to spin in a circle until they fell on their backs, exhausted and dizzy. As they gazed up at the stars, happy beyond words, the white reindeer flung back his head and roared – a cataclysmic sound that scattered the Wayfinders, and set the stars trembling.

It was over. The sorcerer had won. He was free to do whatever he pleased. Crushed and desolate, sick with fear, they felt their world tilt, and begin to slide away. Yet even as Ross despaired, the swan flew in his mind. "He's alive, Tilda. There's still a chance."

~

They hurried through the camp as quickly as the snow allowed, expecting each footstep to be their last, yet they reached the forest track without any sign of the sorcerer.

Stillness gripped the frosted birches, and the pines heavy with snow. All sound was hushed until they approached the Old Ones' spring where a stirring began among the spruces, an anguished murmuring, as though, Tilda suspected, they dared not speak too loudly.

Using snow-heaped branches as cover, Tilda and Ross peered through the lattice of needles. Rymi's soul kin lay among dwarf willows, head resting in the trickle of spring water. If Lys was seeking its healing power, he was too late – the sorcerer was there in the guise of his victim, Kelvan. Ross was bewildered. How could this be happening? The vision, the swan – he was so certain he'd got it right.

While Ross struggled to accept what he was seeing, Tilda was listening as the spruces squabbled. One of them could know what to do, if only she could pick them apart. But they were all speaking at once, growing more and more agitated. She had to try another way. Looking up through the branches of the old spruce Tilda placed her hands on the rough bark, and forced her thoughts into the tangle of voices. *Tree spirits, hear me, I am your kin. Heart in wood, sap in blood, hear me, let me in…*

The sorcerer knew they were there, although it hardly mattered. A pair of bothersome gnats would be more of a threat. No need for their souls now, anyway. In the chaos to come there'd be a surfeit of souls. It was his moment, a triumph to be savoured. Especially this, the final indignity – the deathblow delivered in the form of the fool's apprentice. He leaned closer to whisper in Lys's ear. "Your life, your work, it was all for nothing. Hear that Rymi? All worth nothing." Grasping the broken antler, the sorcerer wrenched back the white reindeer's head. In his other hand something jagged and glassy glinted with demon fire.

Ross was desperate to stop this. But as he had no plan, no brilliant idea, he only became more frustrated. Meanwhile,

Tilda was making progress with the old spruce. It kept saying, *eye* something. Or maybe it was *ice*.

Both of them could see that Rymi's soul kin was fading fast – already the spirit's light was no more than a candle flame. And slowly, slowly, relishing every second, the sorcerer was pressing the blade into the white reindeer's throat.

Then in a heartbeat, everything changed. Tilda had the answer, "Scrystone! Ross, use the scrystone."

By now Ross was frantic. "Use it how?" he hissed. "Message him? Ask him to stop?" Then he remembered Rymi's warning about photos. What was it he said, exactly? It had to be right… Scrabbling in his pocket Ross found the phone, and put it on. Then before he could change his mind he stepped out from among the trees.

"STOP!"

The shout crashed around the grove. The sorcerer looked up. He eyed the black slab. Saw the lad's face lit by a light born in another world. "A magic rock?" he growled, with a vicious smirk. "Think again, Voleheart."

Ross had to be strong. He must not meet those eyes. "It's a scrystone," he said nonchalantly, swiping and tapping with a confidence he didn't feel. "See? I caught the Wayfinders in it."

At once the sorcerer recognised the danger. Fury ripped his borrowed face. He dropped the antler. Started across the ice.

"Hold it there," Ross called, aiming the phone. "*I'm taking your likeness.*"

Tilda saw the flash. Heard the sorcerer curse. She saw his stolen form implode, instantly rendered down to its elements. Nothing was left but his own two souls. They floated for a moment, naked, uncertain. Then at dizzying speed they were sucked into the scrystone.

All Ross could see were dazzling lights. Everything was whirling, blurring – the screen, the Wayfinders, the green fire rising in the black water. He fought to keep the phone but it leapt from his hand. Bounced on the ice. Went spinning towards the water, the unfrozen water, where it slid under the surface and into the liquid fire.

As the trap and its prisoner vanished from sight, a mysterious sound arose from the spruce grove. The trees were rejoicing, voicing high, exultant notes that Tilda and Ross found strangely unsettling. Among the branches of the elder spruce all the offerings were trembling, speckling the tree with pinpricks of light, and brightest of them all was a tiny, silver crescent.

At first Ross and Tilda were too shocked to move. They could only watch as Lys drifted upward, passing between them in a brief glimmer of brightness. They saw the reindeer spirit carried away on the air. Then, overwhelmed by the eerie music and the aura of ancient power, they crept away leaving the sacred grove to the stars.

17

On Shining Fell

Rymi's face was grey. He did not wake when they turned him, first one way and then the other, to remove the bulky coat. He made no sound when they carried him to the sleeping place, pushed extra pelts behind him, or when they covered him with deerskins. Propped up on the bed, he looked as frail as an injured bird.

Whatever Hirta was feeling she kept it to herself. "That is all we can do for now," she said, her face an unreadable mask. "We must eat, or we will be ill too." A search of the hut revealed a frying pan, but not much else. "He seems to live on dried fish," Tilda said. She left to fetch some meat from their tent, while Lumi, who had watched all they did, followed her out. Ross went too, to set about collecting firewood.

All that was left of the wood stack was a blackened crater melted into the snow. Ross rescued a few scraps, and the birch trunks that Lumi had pulled from the bonfire, which he broke up as best he could. Dead twigs from the forest's edge completed his haul. Although it was enough for now they would have to find more soon.

On his return Ross was greeted by a whirlwind, as Fann, leaping hysterically, knocked the firewood out of his arms. Even Larna was excited, rolling on her back among the fallen twigs. The dogs, newly emerged from some hiding place, were overjoyed to be rid of the wolf. "Behave," Hirta scolded. "Rymi needs peace." Then she gave each a whole dried fish to keep them occupied.

While the dogs gnawed at their treats in the shadows, the others ate beside the hearth. They talked over the incredible events, speaking in hushed tones so as not to disturb Rymi. Even so, he became restless, mumbling as if in a nightmare. Hirta went over to take his hand, leaning close to catch his words. It was the same thing, over and over – "He is here, he is here."

"Tell him, the sorcerer is gone for good," Tilda said. "Ross trapped him in the scrystone. The Old Ones took it into the spring."

Hirta tried her best, but Rymi would not be reassured. Although he could barely lift his eyelids he was determined to raise his head. When that failed, he made a whispered request. Hirta found the pouch of seeds and roots, and quickly set to work with the contents. Before long she was back at his bedside with the tonic in a bowl, and a wooden spoon to trickle the liquid into his mouth.

Whatever was in the brew, it seemed to work. Rymi lay still for a while, breathing more evenly. Then all of a sudden he spoke, in a firm, clear voice. "He is here," he said. "The Lightbringer is here."

"Fancy thinking of that old legend," Hirta said, looking worried and bemused in turn. "It must be that potion, giving you dreams." Rymi managed a faint smile. He said it would please him to hear the words. "Then you shall," Hirta replied. "This is the season, after all."

Tilda put down her bowl. "Will it be the old way, Nanna?"

"What other way is there?"

The herders knelt, face to face, spreading their skirts around them. Smiling, they joined hands, two become one, and began to rock gently. Ross, watching through flickering flames, found the rocking motion mesmerising. Without realising it, he was moving with them.

After a while Hirta began to chant. "Sun has sung the birds away – song of earth is snow, song of water stone. Sun has left the darkness here – song of air is frost, song of wind is ice. Sun, your children wish for your fire. Sun, your children long for your dawn. Send us a sign of the winter's turning. Send us a sign of the season to come."

Then Tilda gave the response. "In the long night, the deepest darkest night, this will be the sign – the Lightbringer comes.

His coat is of the sky, the stars are its bright jewels. Through rings of fire he flies on his sled of gold, his reindeer bright as day, his reindeer dark as night. In his hand the Eternal One's flame. Joy he brings. His gift is hope, the promise of the Sun's returning.

In the long night, the deepest, darkest night, an ancient promise is fulfilled, the seasons' round begins anew."

The rocking slowed gradually to a stop. "Words to warm hearts," Hirta said wistfully. "If only it was like that."

"It is," Rymi groaned, "It is like that. He lives, the Lightbringer lives." His head turned slowly on the pillow until he was looking directly at Ross. "He has other names. You know one."

Ross frowned. It couldn't be... Could it? The air rustled as the spirit birds stirred, but only he could see them. They were gathered in a crowd above the bed.

Hirta suspected that Rymi was confused. Stiffly, she got to her feet, and returned to his bedside. Thinking to humour him, she asked if he had seen the Lightbringer with his own eyes.

"Remember Fa's kin?" Rymi whispered. "I was his apprentice. Long ago." Hirta said she did. "He had a duty, a sacred duty. When his time came to go into the hill, he... He passed it to me." The others leaned closer so as not to miss a word, wondering what this duty could possibly be. Yet Rymi hesitated. A secret kept for so long was difficult to share.

Observing him keenly, Hirta noticed how his eyes shone in spite of his frailty. That was the potion, gathering up his energy – probably the very last of his energy. She adjusted the twigs and furs to prop him up more, hoping this would make it easier for him to talk. Sure enough, when the words came it was in a torrent.

"Fa's kin kept the gate of the Sun," Rymi declared. "He was the sentinel. The one who welcomes the Lightbringer. Now, when he arrives, I am the one who greets him." He paused for breath. "At leaf fall, I collect herbs. Prepare medicines. Catch fish. Then I wait. Watch the Great Reindeer. When the star-deer stands on shining fell, that is the sign."

Oh, Rymi, Hirta thought, if only you had trusted me with your secret. You didn't have to be alone all those years.

"When a sentinel is chosen, none should know," Rymi said, as if he saw her mind. "I swore to tell no one, except the one who comes after."

"The sorcerer found out," Tilda said, softly.

"Kelvan was to be sentinel after me," Rymi explained, with a heavy sigh. His eyes closed, and there was silence, except for a crackle from the hearth. In their minds was the fate of the man robbed of everything – his secret, his life, even his souls.

It was a while before Rymi summoned the will to speak again. "Everything Kelvan knew, the sorcerer stole. He crushed us both. Destroyed everything. With nobody to welcome him, the Lightbringer cannot enter our world."

Ross asked if that would matter, a thoughtless question that caused Rymi great distress.

"Matter?" he gasped, as if an arrow had struck him. "Matter? He must be invited in, if we are to feel the Sun's fire again. Without the Lightbringer, would the Eternal One return? What of the seasons then? Chaos." He slumped back, exhausted.

"What would we do without the Sun's blessing? Tilda said. "No new leaves for the reindeer, no summer herbs. No mushrooms and berries. No waterfowl, no songbirds…"

"The long night would never end," Hirta added. "Ice would swallow us all, the forest, the creatures, the reindeer folk."

Ross listened, his heart in his boots. Endless freezing cold, the forest icebound, that was what they dreaded the most. But in this time and place – wherever and whenever it was – they did not know what he knew. "Maybe," he said cautiously, "it wouldn't be colder. Maybe it would get too hot all the time. So hot, it would never snow, ever again."

This shocked them. No snow? Ever? The Old Ones had never warned them of that.

Hirta was first to consider the unthinkable. "Old Ma Frost is our friend. She gives us refuge. The strangers fear her freezing breath, but if the seasons warm, nothing will keep them away. They will come with their books of law, saying the Old Ones' land belongs to them. No room for us. No room for reindeer to roam."

"I only know," Rymi whispered, "someone has to welcome the Lightbringer. Then all will be well."

Ross was perplexed. Something he'd stopped believing in years ago, something everyone knew wasn't true, was turning out to be real after all. He tried to guess how the Lightbringer would look, but it was impossible. All he could think of was that jolly, rotund image.

Abruptly, without any warning, Rymi tried to raise himself up. It was a huge effort, born of desperation, and it took all Hirta's strength to keep him from falling off the bed. "The thread...must...not...be broken..." he gasped, his voice thin as wire. The potion was wearing off, weakness overcoming him. It was awful to see. Rymi fell back on the furs, his forehead clammy with sweat. His skin was grey, his mouth tinged with blue. Helpless in the face of this sudden decline they sat in silence, feeling every laboured breath. Ross wondered if Grandad had looked like that, at the end. He wished he could have been there, if only to hold his hand.

Eventually Tilda broke the tense silence. "The sentinel," she whispered, leaning close to Rymi, "must it be you?" Ross, catching her meaning, nodded eagerly. "We can do it," he said.

~

The starlight cast no shadows as Sula and Miri drew the sleds to shining fell. Up the winding track, under pines weighted with snow, past birches glittering with frost, it was easy to imagine the others who had passed that way – the sentinels at midwinter, the mourners bearing the bodies of those who see.

As the track climbed the trees thinned out, and here, dark boulders peeked out from the snow. Higher still, where no tree could thrive, there was space enough to leave a couple of sledges. At first sight the track seemed set to end there, with no way to the top. But further along they found a steep, narrow path leading up between high rocks.

"Now we must go on foot," Tilda said. "It will not be easy."

Before leaving the reindeer they gave them some food. Tilda held her cupped hands out to Miri, crooning a song to her reindeer with words that Ross could not understand. While Sula munched his lichen Ross talked of their adventure together, calling him the best reindeer ever. In return the deer brushed his nose against Ross's cheek, and huffed into the lad's ear.

With farewells exchanged they left the reindeer, and went to tackle the scramble between the rocks. The way up was treacherous, with snow laid over a layer of ice, so there were slips and falls before they emerged on the top. There a vast snowfield opened out before them, stretching out under a canopy of fiercely glittering stars.

Close by stood an altar – a large, flat-topped stone on which sat three small rocks, holding aloft a larger oval rock. Tilda brushed snow from the stone. Taking the last handful of lichen from her bag, she offered the grey-green ball to the sky, to the four winds, to the sacred hill. Then she placed her offering between the three small rocks.

Ross watched her, wondering what he could give. His phone was gone. He had no more coins. Staring at the flat stone, he noticed a small, bowl-shaped depression in the centre. Something he had would fit there, he was certain. He pulled the spruce cone from his half-moon bag, and made his offering to the sky, the four winds, and the hill. Then he placed the cone upright in the stone bowl.

Tilda smiled her approval. "It seems made for that," she said.

They set off across the snowfield tinted violet by the Wayfinders. There was no track to follow because nobody had been there since the first snow. In places it was deep, making heavy going. Ross lurched from side to side, sinking through the frozen crust with almost every step. Once he fell in up to his armpits, and Tilda had to come and pull him out. "We should have brought snowshoes," she said, admitting that haste had left them unprepared.

They stopped for a moment to catch their breath. Ahead lay their destination, a group of low mounds shrouded in snow. Reindeer antlers, standing starkly against the snow, marked every one. These were the tombs of those who see, where they lay forever in their stony graves. "Their spirits help us," Tilda explained, "so long as we respect their resting place." She looked at Ross. "That is where Rymi will come."

Ross asked if it would be soon.

He is very weak," Tilda replied. She paused, biting her lip. "There is something you should know," she said. "When Rymi goes into the hill, Sula will go with him."

"What do you mean, go with him?" Ross looked again at the antlers. A chill gripped his stomach.

"Rymi needs a reindeer to take him to his ancestors. Perhaps not Sula," she added, seeing his horrified expression. "We could choose another deer." But the seed had been sown.

~

The hut was very warm. Lumi had returned, and lay in his place far from the fire, his head resting on crossed paws. Hirta had shivered as his long tongue scraped the blood off his chest, although she had to admit he hadn't been a nuisance. All the same, she felt those yellow eyes burning, following her every move. She could never have imagined a situation like this, never. Her dogs were outside with the reindeer, while a wolf was in here with her. Truly, the world was turned upside down.

She knelt beside Rymi, and took his hand. To bring him comfort, she talked of the things he would need on the path of souls.

"You will have your white coat, your knife, your belt. And Sula will be with you. I know you care for him." But to her surprise, Rymi became upset. "Not Sula," he gasped. "Not mine. I…give him…to Ross. It is…done."

"No-one goes without a guide," Hirta said anxiously.

Rymi tried to raise a hand, but it fell back limply. "There…" he whispered. Hirta followed his gaze to where the four-hoofed guardian hung. "The deer-star? You want that with you?"

He nodded slowly. "My drum. Keep it…for Tilda."

"Oh Rymi, you will have nothing."

That brought the ghost of a smile.

For a long time Hirta clasped his hand in hers, listening to his juddering breath, watching the firelight waver across his face. There were no more words. His breathing became ever softer, ever more shallow. Shadows closed in as the firelight grew weak, but she could not bear to tear herself away. Yet eventually she was compelled to get up. Fire spirits were always hungry – the logs were hollowed out, almost to ash.

She had planned to ask him about that day. Their special day, when she waited with Ma and Fa, and he never arrived. She had always believed it was because of the spirits. Now she realised it was his way of keeping her safe. Hirta smiled ruefully. None of that mattered now, anyway.

She was placing the last log when the wolf suddenly sat up. Hirta knew, even before she turned around, even before Lumi began to sob out his heart.

Rymi was still. Both his souls had flown.

~

The seven stars of the Bear stood, breathing in the cold, as Tilda and Ross struggled across the top of shining fell. The Wayfinders sent flickering wisps to touch the Great Reindeer, while sparks streaked from the region of Steadfast, shooting stars to greet the solstice. Beyond the pale flames, beyond the falling stars, stretched the vastness of unending space.

The further they went into that world of terrible beauty, the more intense the cold became. Faces ached. Breathing was effortful. Sky danced with snow until their destination, once within reach, seemed to float far away. It was a relief to reach the mounds, where the ones who see slept in the white silence.

While they stood in silent contemplation, awed by the heaped stones and neatly stacked antlers, they noticed minute, pin-sharp glints all around them. Tiny ice crystals were falling in trickles, in showers, out of the restless sky.

"Listen," Tilda said softly. "Can you hear it? The stars are whispering."

Enthralled by silvery notes that were almost beyond hearing, they tried not to move in case the celestial sounds ceased. Glittering specks tingled on their faces, and frosted their deer-hair coats. They felt fresh, rinsed clean.

Spellbound as they were, they would never have noticed what was happening on the altar, even if it had been within sight. Far off, in the shadowy embrace of the stones, the spruce cone was opening. Slowly, precisely, the tough brown scales unfolded. Inside each one was a translucent seed, a glowing, pulsing light. Soon the whole cone had become a bright beacon, transmitting its message from this world to another.

And the message was seen. Near the Great Reindeer's antlers, a flush of delicate white appeared. Quickly it grew in brilliance, casting its veil wide until it was lost to east and west. Flowing curves danced along it, blue, green, pale yellow. Shapes drifted away – melting fringes, comets' tails. A towering wing brushed the hill, twisting rapidly, gathering itself into radiant folds. The snow, grown bright, glowed violet under the Lights.

"If we do this," Tilda said, "we will have to come back. Every year. For always."

Ross nodded. "I know."

The folds drew into a ring, a towering crown of light. Rising against the starry sky, at its centre a cloud of rolling colours hid whatever waited there. As they stared in fear and wonder a voice came into their minds, at once near and far away, like a voice in a dream.

"*Who keeps the Gate of the Sun?*"

This was the moment to say the words. Ross opened his mouth, but nothing came out. The sounds dissolved like snowflakes on his tongue.

"*Who keeps the Gate? Who will let me in?*"

Back in the hut it had seemed so simple. But the reality of what they were about to do was crushing. Unable to move, unable to speak, Ross stared into the crown of fire.

"*Where is the sentinel?*" the voice demanded. "*Let me in, or I will go.*"

Tilda seized Ross's hand. She raised it to the sky. "Here," she called out. "We are the sentinels." She smiled at Ross, and together they spoke Rymi's words.

"In the name of the Old Ones we throw wide the Gate. Be welcome, Lightbringer. Come in."

The cloud split across. Out streamed a host of sprites and spirits and strange, wondrous beings formed of light. In their midst, on a sled of gold, sat the Lightbringer, wrapped in a cloak of deepest blue that gleamed with jewel-like stars. In his raised hand a torch blazed with all the splendour of the returning Sun. Drawing his sled were two reindeer with golden antlers – one bright as noon, the other dark as midnight.

The voice, clear and kindly now, echoed in their ears. *"Sentinels at the Gate, take my fire into your hearts. May the flame never go out."*

High above, the sled hung while the reindeer trod the air with hypnotic slowness. Around it the spirits flowed ceaselessly, a glowing whirlwind.

"New sentinels, I see. What will be my gift to you? Name it, it shall be yours."

This was unexpected. Tilda and Ross were startled, and afraid. What were they supposed to say? What could they say?

The Lightbringer stretched out a hand towards Tilda. *"Creature born of earth and stars, tell of your heart's wish."*

"I… I…" she faltered. Then drawing herself up tall, Tilda said boldly, "All I want is to serve the forest, and all that live there."

"And you, creature of earth and stars. What is your heart's wish?"

One thing filled Ross's mind, pushing aside all others. I want Sula to live. I want him to be my reindeer. But then he thought, what if I never go home, ever?

"Tilda, I'm sorry."

"I understand. You will come back though." She gave him a fierce hug, as though she would never let go. Then

181

suddenly she stepped back, almost pushing him away. "Say it now. The Lightbringer will not wait."

For the first time in ages, Ross missed his phone. He tried, really hard, to fix Tilda's face in his memory. He took a deep breath. "My wish is, I want to go home."

Immediately the two reindeer surged towards him. Gleaming eyes, glinting antlers, the Lightbringer laughing, the torch in his hand brilliant as the Sun – all this Ross saw in an instant. He tried to block the piercing light with his arm. Tilda was calling, "Watch the Great Reindeer." Then something lifted him into the light.

Meanwhile, unnoticed, a raven flew from shining fell, carrying in its beak a perfect spruce cone. The beacon would lie hidden – as it always had, time out of mind – until the sky-wheel brought the star-deer around again.

~

When Ross opened his eyes it was dark. Not totally dark – the glow from a tiny, light-up Christmas tree was enough to hint at the small space. He lay on his back. A draught, cool and fresh, brushed across his face. He could almost smell the stars.

Suddenly he heard footsteps. Coming closer. Grabbing the duvet, he pulled it over himself. Hinges squeaked. A shaft of soft light swept briefly across his eyes, making him squint.

"For heaven's sake, it's freezing in here."

Quickly he dragged the duvet up around his ears. She mustn't see the reindeer-hair coat. But he'd pulled the cover up too far – his boots were sticking out at the end of the bed. Luckily she hadn't switched on the light.

Slippers flip-flapped across the room. The window closed with a clunk. "Only four sleeps to go. You've got to be good, or you-know-who won't bring any presents."

She laughed, knowing it was years since he believed in that. Ross laughed too, as if he did not know better.

"Night, Mum."

"Night, Ross. Sleep tight."

The door closed. The footsteps faded. Ross got up, opened the window, and looked out at the sky. There was Steadfast, and there, the Great Reindeer. The apple tree, dressed with frost, glittered under the multitude of stars. Through its branches shone a silver crescent, a bright coin pushed through the fabric of night. Ross felt in his pocket for the green ointment. When he pulled off the lid, the pot was full.

He took off the mittens, coat, and boots, and stuffed them under his bed. He hadn't decided what to say about the phone, or about any of it really. That was for another day. Still in his clothes, Ross lay down on the duvet and stretched out, clutching the star amulet.

Soon he was in another place. Among pine and birch, in a world of shimmering snow, he watched the sky with Tilda. Above them lay the path of souls, the soft light of the star-drift that arches across the dome of night. At the fork in the path where the great bird hovers a ribbon of swans flew, strong and purposeful. The stolen souls, free at last, were going to their long-desired rest. And leading them was Rymi.

Then forest-Ma with the shining face clothed Tilda and Ross in the coats of ones who see. Side by side, they rode on snow-white reindeer, soaring through a starry sky alive with the torches of the Wayfinders.